The Open University

School of
HEALTH
&
SOCIAL
WELFARE

K100
Understanding Health and
Social Care

Block 3

Care and
Communities

K100 Production Team

Andrew Northedge (Chair)
Jan Walmsley (Deputy Chair)
Margaret Allott (Course Manager)
Tanya Hames (Course Secretary)
Joanna Bornat
Hilary Brown
Celia Davies
Roger Gomm
Sheila Peace
Martin Robb
Deborah Cooper (VQ Centre)

Jill Alger, Julie Fletcher (Editors); Janis Gilbert (Graphic Artist); Hannah Brunt, Rob Williams (Designers); Paul Smith (Librarian); Deborah Bywater (Project Control Assistant); Ann Carter (Print Buying Controller); Pam Berry (Text Processing Services); Mike Levers (Photographer); Vic Lockwood, Alison Tucker, Kathy Wilson (BBC Producers); Maggie Guillon (Cartoonist)

Regional Education and Training Managers

Lindsay Brigham
Anne Fletcher
Carole Ulanowsky

External Assessor

Professor Lesley Doyal, University of Bristol

This is the K100 core course team. Many other people also contributed to making the course and their names are given in the Introduction and Study Guide.

The Open University
Walton Hall, Milton Keynes
MK7 6AA

First published 1998

Designed, edited and typeset by The Open University

Printed and bound in the United Kingdom by Thanet Press Ltd, Margate, Kent

ISBN 0 7492 3422 9

Further information on related Open University courses and study packs may be obtained from the Information Officer, School of Health and Social Welfare, The Open University, Walton Hall, Milton Keynes MK7 6AA.

1.1

17158B/k100b3u10i1.1

Contents

Study skills by Andrew Northedge

Introduction

The main focus of Block 2 was on the ways in which care is provided within people's homes, on the one hand, and in residential and institutional settings on the other. However, as far back as Unit 3, we noted the increasing emphasis within health and social care on the local community as a desirable setting for care services. As we saw there, 'community care' is often a shorthand for informal care provided within people's homes. However, providing services 'in the community' or 'working in the community' for health and social care often means much more than this. In Block 3, we examine what it means for services to be community-based. Unit 10 *Accessing Community Services* explores the kinds of health and care services that are to be found in local communities, and asks how accessible they are to the range of people they are designed to help. Unit 11 *Caring Communities – Fact or Fiction?* discusses the extent to which informal support structures exist within local communities, and the ways in which statutory and voluntary providers can build on and strengthen community networks. Unit 12 *Communities, Diversity and Care* looks at the implications for health and social care services of recognising that local communities are diverse and changing, and are made up of a variety of groups with a range of needs. Finally, Unit 13 *Finding out about Services in the Community* – the skills unit for this block – gives you the chance to investigate the range of health and social care services available in your own local community, and to develop skills in using sources of information.

Unit 10
Accessing Community Services

Prepared for the course team by Jan Walmsley and Tom Heller

While you are working on Unit 10, you will need:
- Course Reader
- Offprints Book
- *The Good Study Guide*
- Block 2, Unit 6
- Wallchart

Contents

Introduction

In this first unit of Block 3 we explore questions of access to community services. To make what might be quite a dry task more challenging we use a fictionalised case study of two people for whom access to community services is particularly problematic. Jim and Marianne are both long-term heroin addicts. Additional problems associated with their addiction are homelessness and physical illness. Their situation raises both practical questions, about how services can be accessed, and moral questions, about entitlement to resources when their problems can be regarded as at least in part self-inflicted.

Core questions

- What barriers are there to access to community health and care services?
- To what extent can people exercise choice in the services they access?
- What strategies exist to promote access to services for people who are disadvantaged?

Jim and Marianne's story is based on a real couple, but heavily fictionalised to protect their identity. Their story is a way of tracking the intricacies of the health and care system through the eyes of people for whom it is supposed to work.

The unit is structured around the careers of Jim and Marianne as users of health and social care, but leads out at various points to the structure, philosophy and practice of other services. The unit ends with a discussion of four strategies for change.

Section 1
Jim and Marianne: testing the limits

1.1 Introducing Jim and Marianne

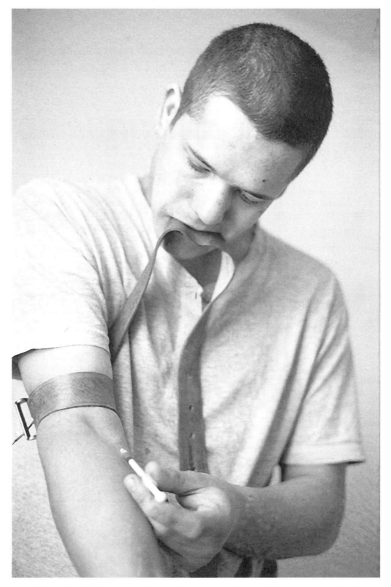

The lifestyles of long-term drug abusers are frequently sensationalised

In the introduction I described Jim and Marianne, our case study for this unit, as 'long-term heroin addicts'. The lifestyles of long-term drug abusers are frequently sensationalised in the media, as in the photograph, and the following extract from *Trainspotting*, a novel about Scottish heroin users that was turned into a hugely successful film:

> *He droaps a cotton ball intae the spoon n blaws oan it, before sucking up*
> *aboot 5 mls through the needle, intae the barrel ay the syringe. He's goat a*
> *fuckin' huge blue vein tapped up which seems tae be almost comin*
> *through Ali's arm. He pierces the flesh and injects a wee bit slowly, before*

suckin blood back intae the chamber. Her lips are quivering as she gazes pleadingly at him for a second or two. Sick Boy's face looks ugly, leering and reptilian, before he slams the cocktail towards her brain.

She pulls back her heid, shuts her eyes and opens her mooth givin' oot an orgasmic groan.

(Welsh, 1993, pp. 8–9)

However, I introduce Jim and Marianne not through a description of such gruesome practices, but through hearing about the people behind the heroin addict label.

Jim and Marianne

Jim and Marianne are a couple. When I met them for the first time they were in their early thirties. They had been together for about ten years. Although they had been having unprotected sex during these years they had no children and Marianne had never become pregnant. They met when they were both in a drug rehabilitation centre on the outskirts of a northern industrial town. They became the 'star pupils' of the centre. They both tried to outdo each other in getting clean from drugs and in striving to become model citizens. They took up all sorts of sporting activities, participated in the groups and in the running of the centre. Eventually, the time to re-enter the community came and they were helped to move into their own flat. Jim was offered a job at the rehabilitation centre itself and Marianne, helped by her family, tried to establish a little business for herself buying and selling things from car boot sales and cheaper antique shops.

Jim described his childhood as 'difficult'. He never knew his father, and he said his mother was unable to cope with him because of her own problems with alcohol. He had spent many of his childhood years in a variety of foster homes and children's homes.

Marianne's parents owned three newsagent shops and were comparatively prosperous. But, according to Marianne, the relationships within her family were not straightforward. Her father had a series of extra-marital affairs, but when his own health deteriorated he came back to be with his wife, Marianne's mother. Their relationship seemed to stabilise but Marianne said they had never been very communicative or demonstrative with each other, or with her, and usually tried to solve problems by spending money on them.

In Jim's words to Marianne:

> I don't know what's better, my family who fucked me up when I was young, or yours who's always muckin' us about now. They really do my head in. I know they don't like me, and blame me for things. They offer us things, but always with strings attached. I think they want you to leave me, and go back to them.

The quality of Jim and Marianne's lives deteriorated after a few years out of the rehabilitation centre. Neither of them could sustain the progress they had made. They found that making friends in the community who were not their old 'junkie' friends was very difficult and they became quite socially isolated. Marianne described her family as supportive in some ways, but the emotional costs of getting help from them seemed to be considerable. Jim felt patronised and Marianne felt unable to really confide in either of her parents and was wary of her brothers and their circles of friends. Together Jim and Marianne slipped back into increasing drug use. Jim lost his job immediately at the rehabilitation centre, which insisted on a drug-free environment, and Marianne found it harder than ever to make a living. Both confessed that they were involved in petty crime at this stage. Their general health started to decline. Marianne found that the sites she was using for injection became persistently infected and she spent several spells in hospital with swollen legs and nasty ulcers. Jim had had a valve problem in his heart since birth. His lungs had been damaged by this and by the repeated chest infections he developed. Both of them had hepatitis C infection, which probably contributed to them feeling low in energy and being susceptible to persistent infections.

Activity 1   **The people behind the label**

Allow about 10 minutes   The account in the case study box is about the people behind the drug addict label.

(a)   Did it change your view of them?

(b)   What advantages do you consider such additional knowledge might have for a health practitioner meeting Jim and Marianne for the first time?

(c)   Can you foresee any problems for a practitioner supplied with this additional information?

Comment   (a)   People who read the course varied in their response. Two said emphatically that they did change their views. Another, accustomed to working with people who are often the subject of negative stereotyping, said: 'I would always seek to find the person behind the label'.

(b)   Maybe a practitioner would have more sympathy with Jim and Marianne than if she had simply been presented with bald medical information – intravenous drug user, faulty heart valve, damaged lungs, infertility, subject to persistent low-level infection.

She might be less inclined to make moral judgements such as 'they don't deserve help' or 'they brought it on themselves'.

The additional information might also suggest a broader range of helpful interventions than straightforward medical treatment: family therapy, even fertility treatment for Marianne, whose childlessness was a cause of regret.

(c)   A practitioner might feel overwhelmed by the plethora of problems. It would be much easier, perhaps, to prescribe some antibiotics, give some advice on diet or suggest a detoxification centre.

She might feel that even if she wanted to do more for them, resources were such that she should confine herself to her immediate remit, treatment for the problem as presented.

You may have recognised echoes of the discussion of the biomedical model in Unit 2. It was suggested there that a doctor working in the biomedical framework would probably act differently from one who took a more holistic approach to patients' problems. The next section takes this discussion further by looking at the moral dilemmas a real practitioner faces when coming into contact with people who clearly need help, but who may be classed as 'difficult'.

1.2 Moral dilemmas

It is clear from the account of Jim and Marianne's lives that they need some help. But do they deserve help? Some of our course testers had very strong reactions to the inclusion of drug users in a course about health and social care. Here is one typical response:

> *I am not sure that Jim and Marianne and people like them deserve this sort of attention. Their problems were self-inflicted. It must have cost someone (we taxpayers?) a lot of money to rehabilitate them, yet they wasted the opportunity, cadged more money off Marianne's parents, stole from honest members of the community, and then expected to be bailed out by the NHS. Are there no limits to the obligations we all have to support people who seem determined to waste their lives, and damage the lives of others as they do so?*

Do you share this attitude? It represents a clear challenge to the idea that everyone has rights to health and social care services simply because they happen to be resident in a community.

This question is one we could debate in abstract terms, but it takes a very concrete form when practitioners have to make decisions about resources, eligibility and priorities. Because I take a particular interest in drug users in my work as a GP, I have some experience of facing the issues. I explore some of them in Chapter 5 in the Reader.

Activity 2 **Tough decisions**

Allow about 20 minutes

Read Chapter 5 in the Reader now. Concentrate on the dilemmas I faced in considering what to do when called out by Julia to examine her child. As this block is about communities, look at the question from two perspectives:

(a) the GP's obligations to the individual

(b) the GP's obligations to the community

and, under these headings, list the considerations involved in coming to a decision about taking Julia and her family on to the practice list.

Comment

Obligations to the individual	**Obligations to the community**
Sick child, no fault of his own	Family will be expensive to treat, means fewer resources to spend on other (more deserving?) patients
Holistic view of Julia's situation suggests she needs help	Doctors should focus on things they can treat rather than trying to take on the troubles of the world
Julia is asking for help for the first time, responding to an empathetic doctor	Should not reward a deviant who has brought her troubles on her own head
May be an opportunity to stop this family sliding deeper into the mire	May be a constant drain on public money with no real return

No other agencies available to offer support	Democratically elected local authority has taken the decision to withdraw helping agencies; doctor should go with this consensus

In theory, everyone has the right to register with a GP practice, and expect treatment – something we examine in more detail below. There are other things to think about too.

- It is not just Julia whose welfare is at stake: her children may be at some kind of risk. Any health or social care worker in contact with Julia's family will have to be aware of the Children Act 1989 principle that 'the child's welfare is paramount' (Department of Health, 1989a), and act accordingly. In the case of the GP this will mean checking with the health visitors attached to the practice, and asking them to visit. They will be obliged to take action if Julia is not providing the care that a 'reasonable parent' should supply under the circumstances.

- In this sort of situation a GP may be professionally liable if things were to go wrong and the child became seriously ill as a result of negligence.

- On this occasion my own needs, and those of my family, had to be put aside, but neither a GP nor any other health or social care worker can sustain this level of commitment to the welfare of others indefinitely.

- In the Reader chapter I also reflect on why I am attracted to work with drug users. Is it solely out of altruism, or does this aspect of my work feed an unworthy personal need? And does that matter?

This chapter shows that just one small encounter can present a practitioner like me with a whole host of moral dilemmas. It is well nigh impossible to draw hard and fast rules when every case is different, and when personal as well as professional issues come into play. Legal requirements, such as the Children Act, mean that the question is not just a matter of individual judgement.

Moreover, such decisions have to be made not only at the face-to-face level, but in planning how to use limited resources.

Activity 3   **Rationing resources**

Allow about 5 minutes   As a member of a health authority responsible for purchasing health services you are faced with a contracting budget. Given a choice between retaining an eight-bed drug rehabilitation centre (where someone like Julia could get treatment) and setting up four additional beds for acute psychiatric care, which would you choose?

Comment   This dilemma was faced by one health authority in 1997. The decision was to close the drug rehabilitation centre in favour of financing acute psychiatric care. Did you make the same choice?

If you did make the decision that Jim and Marianne, Julia and her children, are less deserving than people with acute psychiatric conditions, where would you draw the line? At treatment for motorists who drink or drive recklessly; cyclists who do not wear helmets;

smokers; people who eat too much fatty food, or indulge in sports like ski-ing or horse riding, which carry a high risk of injury?

If you knew that a place in prison, where many drug users spend time, costs up to £30,000 a year, would that influence your decision?

1.3 Testing the limits

Choosing Jim and Marianne as the central case study in the unit was a deliberate strategy to enable you to consider conflicts at the very heart of health and social care:

- the rights of the individual versus the rights of the community

- the nature of community for people who have no settled abode

- dilemmas about apportioning limited resources.

Following their story is a way of testing the limits of health and social care services, and exploring where community obligation should stop.

There are considerable moral and ethical issues involved in the debates around this case study. Do citizens have unlimited calls on health service resources, or are there limits to what services and facilities people could or should expect from the state? Do people whose problems may be considered to be 'self-inflicted' have the same rights and access to resources as other people? We will be reconsidering such questions at various points in the unit.

Key points

- An approach that seeks to find the person behind the label is an antidote to their being seen simply as a collection of 'problems'. It may also make a practitioner's task more complex.

- Heavy drug users test the limits of community services.

- Practitioners and planners are faced with moral dilemmas that are not susceptible to hard and fast rules.

- When children are involved, the welfare of the adult patient or client is not the sole consideration.

Study skills: Reading towards your essays

With TMA 02 only just behind you, perhaps it seems untimely to raise the topic of assignments now. Yet, as you launch yourself into another block, this is a good moment to stop and think about how your essay writing fits into your studies as a whole. Did your recent essay feel like a last-minute panic, or had you been building up to it gradually during the previous weeks? Are there ways to build essay writing into your work on the whole block?

One possibility is to look at TMA 03 right now. The questions on offer may not make complete sense to you before you have read the block, but you can still try underlining key words in pencil and start jotting down a few thoughts straight away. This will focus your mind and help you to recognise what might be useful for your essay as you work through the units. If you have an 'Essay' folder, then, as you study the block, you can keep adding in new ideas as you jot them down. Then, by the time you reach the writing stage, you will have a good basis from which to build your essay. Also, having the essay titles in mind will give you a stronger sense of purpose as you read. It will also help to shape your ideas and opinions, so that they are more fully developed when you need them for writing your essay.

It would be wrong to see the whole course as shackled to the essays, or to regard what is not relevant to the essays as not worth knowing. But being aware of the essay questions gives an extra thrust to your studies – a purpose to your reading and an edge against which to hone your thoughts. As we said earlier, writing essays is a key part of the learning process, and you can make it work for you all the way through each block.

Section 2
Accessing primary care

This section is about gaining access to primary care, one service that is open to every member of the population as of right. First, we pick up Jim and Marianne's story again.

Homeless

Jim and Marianne's problems worsened when they became homeless. It happened like this.

Jim and Marianne decided to move away from their old haunts and try to make a new start in Sheffield. Marianne's parents gave them the deposit on a small flat above a chip shop and also the first week's rent. Marianne said that her mother wanted them to have the money but her father was resistant, saying that it would just get wasted, as it had been all the other times they had given them anything in the past.

Unfortunately, her father was proved right. Jim and Marianne were not used to having so much cash in hand; they spent most of the money on heroin and were evicted. They found a place to sleep and store their few possessions in an old potting shed at the corner of a disused allotment on the edge of town. But conditions deteriorated with the onset of autumn. The ground was muddy around the shed and they thought they had been spotted by one of the Allotment Committee members. Jim's chest started to play up again, he began coughing up horrible green stuff, and became quite low and unmotivated in his mood. Marianne's leg ulcers took a turn for the worse.

They decided to get their health sorted out properly ...

2.1 What is primary care?

Jim and Marianne's first and most obvious port of call is their GP surgery. Even people who have little local knowledge usually know that there will be a doctor's practice locally. Jim and Marianne find that the GP practises in a modern purpose-built health centre. The Information Booklet in the waiting area tells them that it supplies 'primary care services' and that there are four other GPs in the practice, which serves the suburbs and the villages beyond. In addition to the GPs, the staff comprises:

- a practice manager
- three clerks/receptionists
- two practice nurses
- a counsellor who works three days a week at the centre.

The practice also supplies on-site physiotherapy, chiropody, minor operations and child psychiatry from professionals who visit at regular intervals.

A health centre

What the booklet did not explain, because it is assumed that everyone knows the answer, is what is meant by 'primary care services'.

Primary care

Although the booklet in the surgery assumed most people know what is meant by the term 'primary care', an exact definition can be surprisingly hard to pin down. Barbara Starfield, an American public health academic, has proposed this definition:

> *Primary care is first-contact, continuous, comprehensive, and co-ordinated care provided to populations undifferentiated by gender, disease, or organ system ...*
>
> (Starfield, 1994, p. 1129)

This differentiates primary care from 'secondary' services usually provided within hospitals. In addition to this definition Starfield has described the four functions of primary care that together define it uniquely:

> *These four functions are the point of first contact for all new needs, person focus rather than disease focussed care over time, providing care for **all** needs that are common in the population, and coordinating care for both those needs and for needs that are sufficiently uncommon to require special services.*
>
> *(Starfield, 1995, p. 3)*

The box below summarises the advantages and disadvantages of each of these functions as they operate in the UK.

The four functions of primary care

First point of contact for all new needs

The existence of a practice list, whereby most people in the UK have a named GP, ensures that entry to secondary services is controlled. Compared with direct entry to specialist services, as happens in some other countries, this method is cost-effective. Self-referral to specialist services can lead to expensive duplication of investigations and even unnecessary surgical intervention (Franks *et al.*, 1992). Potential disadvantages might include denial of referral to a relevant specialist or refusal to consider the need for a second opinion.

Person focus rather than disease-focused care over time

Person-focused care is said to lead to better recognition of people's problems, more consistent preventive care, better communication between physician and consulting person, less inappropriate use and less hospitalisation ... and more satisfaction all round. Possible disadvantages are that a generalist (GP) might miss a serious illness which would have been spotted by a specialist who was focusing on disease manifestation rather than on the person.

Providing care for all needs that are common in the population

This has many obvious advantages. A comprehensive service serves the needs of the whole population. Even when there may be competing demands on resources, a unified service can ensure a rational evaluation of those demands. Possible disadvantages might be that no single person or service can know everything about all conditions ... is it all spread a little thin this way?

Co-ordinating care for primary care needs and for needs that require special services

Co-ordinating care ensures that the primary care workers are aware of special referrals that are made and assist in making them, and provide information that helps the specialist come to the correct conclusions. When information is returned from the specialist this can be discussed with the person who has attended. The benefits include greater efficiency of care and less likelihood of adverse effects resulting from incompatible recommendations and treatments. Possible disadvantages are that the system relies on good communication between specialist and primary care services, and, if for any reason the individual is denied access to primary care services, they will have great difficulty accessing other more specialist medical services.

Activity 4   The functions of primary care

Allow about 20 minutes   Using the information in 'The four functions of primary care' box to guide you, write a few notes on the possible advantages and disadvantages of each of the four functions of primary care as far as Jim and Marianne are concerned:

(a)   first point of contact for all new needs

(b)   person focus rather than disease-focused care over time

(c)   providing care for all needs that are common in the population

(d)   co-ordinating care for primary care needs and for needs that require special services.

Comment   (a)   *First point of contact for all new needs.* Jim and Marianne know where to go for their health needs (as you will see, this is not necessarily the case with community care services). They won't feel singled out because the service is used by almost everyone. The disadvantage is that if they meet an unhelpful or judgemental response, their access to other services or specialist forms of medical care might be barred.

(b)   *Person focus rather than disease-focused care over time.* You may have considered this in the discussion of the person behind the label in Section 1. Jim and Marianne seem to need people within the formal services who can appreciate them as individuals, rather than who simply respond to their immediate medical needs. It would be easy to see them as a collection of symptoms and pathologies, and miss the point that they are human beings who need medical treatment because of a complex interplay of factors. However, they might prefer to have only their medical symptoms attended to, rather than have their whole lives opened to scrutiny by strangers.

(c)   *Providing care for all needs that are common in the population.* Can one service even begin to meet everyone's needs? Jim and Marianne's needs are not especially common, particularly in the leafy suburb where their surgery is situated.

(d)   *Co-ordinating care for primary care needs and for needs that require special services.* For Jim and Marianne, having a central co-ordinating primary care service could be enormously helpful. It ensures, for example, that the various hospital services they require report back to a single place. All their hospital reports will come back to the health centre and the workers there will be able to review their current state of health at any time. On the other hand, if they are unfortunate in their choice of GP, or cannot get one at all, they might lose out entirely.

You may well not recognise the service you get from your GP in this description of primary care, because in many cases it represents an ideal to be aspired to, rather than reality. In the rest of the section you will see whether this ideal works for Jim and Marianne.

The ideal GP?

2.2 Patients' rights

One of the implications of the primary care model is that GPs control access to a range of medical services. They perform a 'gate-keeping' function, determining whether someone should get specialist treatment. Indeed, in order to be eligible for some state benefits, such as Mobility Allowance, a doctor's signature to a statement of medical need is a prerequisite. For people in need of health care, getting on to a GP list is obviously crucial. Technically this should not be a problem, because the Patient's Charter guarantees certain rights. These are listed in the box overleaf.

GP services: patients' rights

- Everyone living in the UK has the right to be registered with a GP (General Practitioner). You can choose your doctor, provided that person agrees to accept you. Lists of GPs can be found with your local [health authority], Community Health Council, Citizens Advice Bureau, library or main post office. If you are without a GP, your [health authority] must find you one within two working days.

- Your GP should provide a leaflet setting out the services the practice offers.

- You are entitled to a [free] health check when you first join a doctor's list.

- You have the right to see a GP (not necessarily your own) at any time during surgery hours, unless there is an appointment system. In this case you must be given an appointment for a later surgery, providing the delay will not put your health at risk.

- You can ask your GP for a home visit, but you have no automatic right to one. Your doctor must visit you if it is necessary on medical grounds. If you are over 75 you are entitled to an annual home visit and health check.

- When the surgery is shut the practice must provide an emergency service at all times.

- When you are away from home for up to three months you can ask a GP to accept you as a temporary patient. A doctor who won't accept you must still give you any treatment that is immediately necessary.

- You have the right to change doctor easily and quickly. If you move, apply to a GP in your new area. If you are unhappy with your GP you can change without giving a reason. Your [health authority] must find you an alternative GP or send you details of how to change and a list of doctors within two working days. Once you have changed they should send any of your records urgently needed by your new doctor within two working days and transfer remaining records within six weeks.

- You can also be removed from a GP's list without a reason being given, but the [health authority] must make sure you are not without a doctor.

(Association of Community Health Councils for England and Wales, 1994)

As I said above, unlike most of the services in health and social care you have encountered so far in the course, primary care is available to all. It has the great advantage of being universal. Almost everyone, white or black, rich or poor, old or young, can use primary care services. There is no stigma attached to going to your doctor, as there often is to, say, approaching a clinic for sexually transmitted diseases, being a child 'in care' or attending a psychiatric service.

But you might like to reflect on the force of some of these 'rights'. You have a right to be registered, provided that the doctor agrees to accept you – but the GP also has a right to refuse you, and does not have to justify his or her refusal.

It could be considered that not only are patients' rights restricted in practice, but also they only cover a limited range of interactions.

Activity 5 **Receiving Jim and Marianne**

Allow about 10 minutes What response might Jim and Marianne get when approaching a primary care centre you know? Try to base your responses on your own experiences of local services rather than on stereotypical views.

Comment Our course testers thought that there would be a great range of issues raised and potential responses. Some predicted a thoroughly negative and potentially hostile response, while others thought they would be treated in the same way as any other people seeking help:

> *'Our local team always seems so warm and inviting to all comers. I expect Jim and Marianne would get a similar welcome.'*

> *'It all depends who is on the desk and who they get to meet. Some of the staff and doctors are wonderful, but others I should think would make their lives pretty uncomfortable.'*

> *'I've recently moved and had difficulty finding a doctor because they are so territorial. How would J and M manage without an address?'*

> *'Practice boundaries have tightened. My downstairs neighbour's doctor refused me as 'out of his area'. The reception at my new doctor's was rather like immigration control when I signed on. The woman in front of me, who was black, was registering for herself and her sister (currently out of the country). She was being asked very detailed questions about places and dates of residence for herself and her sister and being quoted prices in case she had to pay. Presumably it wasn't a racist thing as neither of the practice doctors is white.'*

> *'Our doctors and their team would make sure that they knew that they were unwelcome, largely because they will be so costly to treat. They would try to get shot of them by making them feel stigmatised and just about frozen out.'*

So, new patients cannot always be sure of a warm welcome. Below, we examine some factors that influence people's ability to access primary care.

2.3 Geography, attitudes and resources

In practice, people like Jim and Marianne can have great difficulty in exercising their 'rights' to primary health care. The responses to Activity 5 refer to three factors that will make their right to access the primary care service problematic:

- geography
- attitudes
- resources.

Each of these is examined in turn.

Geography

Difficulty in accessing services is partly a matter of where people live. Despite good intentions such as 'Services should not vary widely in range or quality in different parts of the country' (Department of Health, 1996, p. 8), inner-city areas often have far lower standards of primary care than the medical centre described above; often a GP will be working single-handedly in poorly adapted premises.

In addition, any practice will almost certainly restrict access on the grounds of where people live. Most practices have a catchment area. Beyond this circumscribed area it is considered impractical to take on new patients because of possible problems with, for example, home visiting.

Homeless people like Jim and Marianne have particular difficulty registering with services that are based on the notion of a geographical community with spatial boundaries. We considered the significance of homelessness in Unit 6. Not having an address is a real problem when almost all registration processes require it. A 1996 report for Shelter, the voluntary organisation concerned with providing decent housing for all, showed that while 97 per cent of the population as a whole are registered with a GP, approximately 70 per cent of homeless people were not. Reasons cited by respondents were that they were told the doctor's list was full, or they were not allowed to fill in the forms by the receptionist. As a result, the report shows, most homeless people rely on hospital accident and emergency services for health care, with the result that they do not get a co-ordinated response or access to other services that primary care provides. As one care worker interviewed for the survey commented:

> *The problem is that the GP is the gatekeeper to the NHS these days – if you haven't got a doctor you're in trouble.*

> *(North et al., 1996, p. 5)*

Attitudes

As our course testers' responses to Activity 5 suggest, not all teams or individual health professionals have a positive attitude towards treating people with drug-related problems. Some of the barriers to GP involvement have been identified in various reports.

A survey of GPs in Greater Manchester (Davies and Huxley, 1997) reported that 20 per cent of GPs did not prescribe for opiate users; 11 per cent believed that opiate users should be removed from the practice list; and 45 per cent believed that treatment of opiate users was beyond the competence of GPs. Drug users themselves may be reluctant to register with a GP because they see them as unsympathetic (McKeganey, 1988).

In a study in Scotland (Greenwood, 1992) other reasons given included GPs' difficulty in establishing rapport and fears of being taken advantage of, the potential for deceit, disgust at injecting practices, fear of contracting HIV, fear of censure from colleagues for substitute prescribing, possible effect on other patients in the practice and disillusionment at patients' relapses.

Implicit value judgements might also be made.

- Are these people going to be time-consuming, 'demanding' or problematic to the practice? The fear might be that they will use up an excessive amount of the energies of the staff.

- Is there a threat of violence or disruptive behaviour? Many people's views of drug users are stereotypical and those who come into contact with them may initially imagine that they will be more violent than other people.

- Might drug users somehow affect the experience of other people who attend the health centre? If there are large numbers of drug users on the premises, might this make other attenders feel threatened or less comfortable in some way?

These are all fears that many providers of health care services might share. They are not necessarily borne out by research. For example, although there are increasing reports of violence perpetrated on primary care staff (Kidd and Stark, 1995), there is no evidence that this is particularly due to people with drug-related problems. There is, however, evidence that drug users do use primary care services more often than people who do not use opiates (Leaver *et al.*, 1992).

Resources

Jim and Marianne are likely to need more than average amounts of drugs, person time, hospital referrals and the like. We made a start on listing their medical needs in Activity 1. Just to remind you, medical support might involve:

- infertility advice
- cardiology referral for Jim's heart
- nursing help with Marianne's ulcers
- liver specialist referral for their hepatitis problems.

There can be no avoiding the fact that any primary care team Jim and Marianne approach for help will be aware that becoming involved with them will involve a considerable commitment of time, energy and expense.

Such issues have acquired more urgency as greater emphasis is placed on costing services supplied through primary care. Many arrangements for organising and delivering primary care services introduced in the late 1980s and 1990s had as their explicit purpose the need to control and keep account of the costs of the services provided. The intention was to make all GPs and other members of primary health care teams aware of the costs of the facilities that are under their control, or to which they might wish to make referrals. For example, all doctors receive a monthly statement of the amount that they have spent on medication, how this compares with their expenditure in the previous year and how it compares with other doctors' expenditure, both in their own area and nationally. Also, many health authorities restrict the amount that primary health care teams can spend on the salaries of the people working in the team, and there are controls on other items of primary care expenditure.

In addition to these general financial measures, many general practices (including the one Jim and Marianne approached) have an element of control over their own budgets. These arrangements are at the time of writing (1997) known as 'fund-holding'.

What is fund-holding?

Fund-holding GPs have a budget allocated to their practice annually to pay for drugs, most hospital services, district nurses and health visitors and practice staff. This means that they are both purchasers and providers, to use the terms introduced in Unit 3. The amount of money allocated to each practice is determined by past usage and adjusted according to the number of patients on the practice list. Fund-holding enables GPs to choose which hospitals and clinics they refer patients to, and to expand services offered at the health centre or surgery; it is also said to enable them to be more responsive to patient needs and choices.

An Audit Commission report into GP fund-holding identified such disadvantages as costly administration and the inability of many fund-holding GPs to manage the complex systems. The report did not find that GP fund-holder patients got preferential treatment, however, which had been a widely expressed fear (Audit Commission, 1996).

It is not hard to imagine that new people joining the practice list, such as Jim and Marianne, could be seen as significant challenges to already limited resources. Certainly, compared with others applying to join the list, they may well require more staff resources, more money spent on their medication and may also require a series of referrals to other agencies. The income that is generated for the practice by two people joining the list, however, is not dependent on their clinical needs. So the practice will be paid exactly the same amount for Jim and Marianne as for any other couple of the same age, living in the same area.

The ideal of community services for all is in theory met by the way primary care services are organised in the UK. But issues of geography, attitudes and resources mean that in practice the ideal is not always the reality.

2.4 Jim and Marianne: experiences of primary care

We have spent some time considering factors that might influence how Jim and Marianne, and others like them whom services perceive as 'difficult', are received by primary care services. So what actually happened?

Here is what Jim and Marianne had to say when asked about their experiences of approaching various GP practices:

> *[Jim speaking] Over the years we have had a really wide range of responses from the different GPs we have had to approach. I know we look rather rough these days, but we are not stupid. When I was working in the rehab house I used to go along to various health centres with the clients from there and act as their advocate, so I do know what I am talking about. But sometimes you are just treated like something the cat has just brought in. It is demoralising and just makes me feel even worse about myself than before. All the time I get nervous about what I should say and I end up feeling tense. Most of the time I would just rather not go. Many of them [GPs] are just bastards, and they don't want us mucking up their clean carpets.*

> *[Marianne] We've been in just about all the hospitals in the area over the years, and tried out quite a few GPs too. It's difficult when they get to know you're using. I always think people are talking about us. The nurses and receptionists sometimes put you at the back of the queue, you watch everyone going in before you. Sometimes, when I'm in a bad way, I don't think it's worth the bother.*

> *But when you do get a good one, one you can sort of settle down with, that's really good. They are not all crap, but even with the good ones you are a bit on edge wondering if you have said the right thing and sort of apologising just for being there at all.*

You'll recall the discussion in Unit 4 of doctor–patient scripts, and the power doctors appear to exert in defining what is, and what is not, permissible behaviour in a consultation. Even once Jim and Marianne had penetrated the barriers to entering the presence of the doctor, it seems that some doctors were well defended against being overwhelmed by, or even sympathetic to, their predicament.

There is a tension between enabling the users of services to access the services they need and the competing imperative to control, manage and contain services within a managerial and cost-limited framework. This tension is apparent in the struggle that Jim and Marianne may have in obtaining satisfactory help with their problems, even in a service such as primary care which sets out to be available to each and every member of the community.

How far might the barriers identified in relation to Jim and Marianne apply to anyone? Some of the issues thrown up by their story are peculiar to people who are seen as difficult or deviant, but the geographical basis of primary care can present problems to people moving house, while any patient depends heavily on the skill and willingness to listen of the GP, the crucial gatekeeper to a range of health services.

Section 3 explores some issues in accessing community care services, which, unlike primary care, do not aspire to be universal.

Key points

- Primary health care is defined as first contact, continuous, comprehensive and co-ordinated care provided to all.

- Primary health care is available as of right to everyone resident in the UK. Nevertheless, some 'deviant' groups, such as drug users, may find it hard in practice to get accepted on to a GP's list. Even moving house can be a barrier.

- A health care system that depends on primary care as the first and co-ordinating point of contact has advantages in terms of accessibility to the majority of the population but, for some disadvantaged groups, it may also be a barrier to obtaining medical help.

- Services that serve geographical communities are hard for homeless people to access.

- Primary health care teams vary in their approach to their patients – access may depend too much on the personal philosophy of the GP.

- Moves to make expenditure on health care the responsibility of individual practices mean that primary health care teams may be reluctant to take on patients who appear to be expensive to treat.

Section 3
Accessing community care

This section asks what issues individuals like Jim and Marianne may encounter as they try to access care in the community in which they happen to live.

First of all, we catch up with Jim and Marianne's story again, as they move from being patients of primary care to becoming users of community care services.

Crisis

Unfortunately, things did not work out well for Jim and Marianne. Jim's defective heart valve became infected (sub-acute bacterial endocarditis) and an infected embolus was thrown from the aortic valve into the left side of his brain. He had a stroke, which affected his speech and many functions on the right-hand side of his body.

Marianne said:

> I thought Jim was gonna die, he looked that awful. He lost even more weight and looked kind of sick yellow, you could see the bones in his face. Anyone looking at him would think he's got AIDS or something. He walks funny and talks like he's drunk all the time. He keeps getting in moods, fighting with the doctors.

Marianne was no luckier. The injection site in her right groin failed to heal. She had increasing problems injecting there, but all her other veins were thrombosed long before. During a particularly problematic injecting session, while she was tired and anxious about Jim, she punctured her left femoral artery. This in turn thrombosed and she was rushed to hospital, where it was decided to amputate ...

At one stage both Jim and Marianne were in hospital at the same time. Jim was in the Stroke Rehabilitation Unit, based in a small community hospital. He made good progress. His speech returned almost completely, although he still slurred some words, making him sound rather drunk when he was tired. His mood was affected and he was often sullen and withdrawn and easily became irritable and verbally aggressive. Although he could move around inside the unit, using items of furniture for support, he was not really strong enough to venture out on his own: he could not cross roads or carry shopping. Marianne was under the care of specialist vascular surgeons who amputated her right leg at thigh level. For her period of rehabilitation and intensive physiotherapy, while waiting for her new limb to be fitted, she was transferred to the District General Hospital. Unfortunately, because the amputation was necessarily at a very high level through her right hip, she was unable, finally, to use her prosthesis and was told she would have to use a wheelchair for the rest of her life.

'What a pair we are', said Marianne immediately after her amputation. 'To think we used to be fit and healthy. We biked everywhere. Up the big hills and all. What a way to live. I wouldn't do it to a dog.'

3.1 Entering the system

In this section we examine some of the barriers to accessing good-quality community care that Jim and Marianne might experience. Unlike the world of primary health care, with which she and Jim were all too familiar, community care was a new concept to Marianne. I am going to take you through some of the issues she and Jim are likely to encounter as they cross from primary health care services that (almost) everyone uses to services reserved for that minority of adults who need extra help.

We pick up Jim and Marianne's story at the point they were discharged from hospital. Although they entered hospital with the label of substance abusers or drug addicts, when they left they had in practice entered a new category from a service provider's point of view, that of people with impaired mobility. Jim was not really strong enough to get out and about or carry shopping, and Marianne was in a wheelchair. In a sense, they made the transition from being, perhaps, marginal to social care to being physically disabled, one of the classic groups for whom community care provides. Ironically, you might argue that in community care terms Marianne was fortunate to have her leg amputated. Not only did it save her life, it also meant that she qualified for assistance under the Chronically Sick and Disabled Persons Act 1970, which makes it a duty of local authorities to make an assessment of a person deemed to be disabled, whether or not they request it. If she had remained able-bodied she would merely be, in the eyes of the law, homeless, and might, at worst, have been discharged from hospital to make her own way on the streets. Jim's position is more ambiguous. He might qualify in his own right – he might also expect support if he were to be designated as Marianne's carer. You will recall from Unit 1, Section 3, that the Carers (Recognition and Services) Act 1995 requires the needs of carers to be the subject of a separate assessment if requested.

What can they expect now that they are part of community care?

First, it will be helpful to refresh your memory about how community care is intended to operate under the NHS and Community Care Act 1990 (see Care in the UK). From the user's point of view key aims of the new system were:

- to enable people to live as independently as possible in their own homes or 'homely' settings in the community (Department of Health, 1989b, p. 3)

- 'to give people a greater say ... in how they live their lives and the services they need to help them to do so' (Department of Health, 1989b, p. 4)

- to enable users and carers to 'exercise the same power as consumers of other services' (Social Services Inspectorate/Scottish Social Work Group, 1991, p. 11).

In other words, the central aims were to give users of the system more power to make choices, something that has loosely been termed 'empowerment'. How far are Jim and Marianne likely to be able to realise these ideals? First, we look at some difficulties they might have in obtaining information. Then we look at barriers in the process of needs assessment.

3.2 Obtaining information: community care plans

One place to which Jim and Marianne might turn for information about their rights and entitlements, now they are community care users, is the community care plan which all social services departments are obliged to develop and publish.

Activity 6   Community care plans

Allow about 20 minutes

Offprint 14 is an extract from one local authority's 1996/7 community care plan. In fact, Jim and Marianne might fit into any one of three service user categories in the plan – 'Services for people with mental health problems', 'Services for people with drug or alcohol problems' or 'Services for people with disabilities'. We have reprinted only the third of these, as Jim and Marianne entered the system with the 'disabilities' label. Read Offprint 14 now, then use your knowledge of Jim and Marianne to make an assessment of how useful it might be to them as a basis for knowledge of what they can expect as newcomers to community care services.

Comment

I imagine Jim and Marianne might find the document less than helpful. For a start, a lot of the information is about people with learning disabilities, numerically the largest single group of users, and is irrelevant to them. Second, I wondered how they would find the language. Abbreviations such as 'F and CS' (Family and Community Services [Department]), although explained in the Introduction to the plan, are obscure, and there are a number of other jargon terms, such as 'Single Regeneration Budget' and 'integrated care management'.

The paragraph headed 'Assessment and care management' gives no useful information to people like Jim and Marianne, except perhaps to illuminate any problems they may be experiencing as they are handed from health to social services managed provision.

The paragraph headed 'Home support services' may indicate that they can expect some kind of help in their home, if and when they get one, and the following paragraph on 'Equipment and adaptations' is similar. But neither the range of assistance they can expect nor the process for obtaining it is spelt out in enough detail to be of practical assistance.

'Day time services' is again largely concerned with learning disability services. It is unlikely that the brief description of options outlined for those with physical disabilities will attract Jim and Marianne.

'Respite care' may in time seem to be important, but there is no obvious 'carer' here. I suggested that Jim might eventually come to see himself as a 'carer', but it is very early days for this to seem a likely option.

'Housing' should be of prime interest. Again, the plan gives very little useful information to people in Jim and Marianne's position.

'Health services' is an area Jim and Marianne know well. Perhaps they might like to know whether they can turn to their primary care service for help. There is no answer here.

One of the aims of the 1990 community care reforms was to provide a mechanism for consultation, collaboration and better provision of information for people who use services and their carers. A principal means of doing this was through publication of an annually revised

SHEFFIELD'S
COMMUNITY CARE SERVICES

SERVICE CHARTER

*A*ll the agencies who are involved in Community Care in Sheffield want to make sure that you get the best quality services that can be provided with the resources available. All the providers in Sheffield have agreed to publish charters, so you'll know what kind of service you can expect to receive.

We believe it is important that you have a clear idea of what standards you can expect from Community Care services. For this reason we are publishing a statement which sets out in general terms what we are trying to achieve.

The rights and expectations under the Charter are broken down into six standards. These are described in detail in a leaflet available from F&CS Information Services, telephone 273 4969. Listed below are the main points under the six Charter Standards:

As a service user, you have the right to expect:

▶ *To be treated fairly with courtesy and respect for your dignity, privacy, cultural and religious beliefs.*

▶ *To be consulted and have your views considered, and to have information provided treated in confidence.*

▶ *To have clear information regarding the services provided, in languages other than English and formats other than print.*

▶ *To ask for an assessment of your needs.*

▶ *To be consulted as part of the assessment process, have your views considered and ask for a review of the assessment.*

▶ *To be able to comment or complain about services.*

▶ *Prompt remedial action if services do not come up to the standards laid down.*

And as a service user, we expect you:

▶ *To notify the provider as quickly as possible if you for any reason have to cancel an appointment.*

▶ *To behave courteously and reasonably towards other service users and towards employees and contractors.*

These rights and expectations form the main points of the Community Care Charter. For a leaflet giving full details of the Standards under the Community Care Charter contact F&CS Information Services, telephone 273 4969.

Community Care Charters are being published by all the following organisations in Sheffield - Family and Community Services Department, Housing Department, Sheffield Health Authority, Community Health Sheffield, South Yorkshire Probation Service, Sheffield Hospital Trusts, and Private, Charitable and Voluntary organisations throughout the city.

community care plan. In preparing a community care plan a social services authority must:

- consult with a number of bodies, including any voluntary bodies that appear to represent users and carers
- ensure that information about community care services is easily available
- ensure that such information is made available in a form that is readily understandable.

However, Gwyneth Roberts, in reviewing community care plans, argues that there is uncertainty about the audiences for whom the plans are designed. One purpose is to aid the local authority's business planning (something you'll read more about in Block 5), and the other is to provide the public with information. In practice, these two purposes are pretty incompatible, and she writes that most community care plans are 'barely accessible to the general population' – let alone people with low levels of literacy, or poor concentration, who make up quite a proportion of users of community care services (Roberts, 1996 p. 158). She found that few plans were available in minority languages, or in Braille or on audio tape or video.

The plan illustrated in Offprint 14 is by no means the worst plan we found. It was not published in any language other than English, but the Community Care Charter included in it is translated into five other languages. However, it seems to fall short of meeting its purpose of providing the sort of information that will enable Jim and Marianne to make informed choices.

What of the assessment process? Will that offer them choices?

3.3 The assessment process

Of course, Jim and Marianne won't be on their own in finding out about services, nor will they be able to access them without a 'needs assessment', a process you read about in Unit 3. During Marianne's stay in hospital the social services department was informed that she was in need of a community care assessment. Marianne was allocated to a care manager whose job was to conduct a needs assessment. A needs assessment is intended to offer service users the opportunity to exercise informed choice:

> Assessment is ... a key part of the process of translating the general duty to provide or arrange community care services within a particular area into a specific service or package of services for a particular individual.

> (Roberts, 1996, p. 159)

Carried out properly, with the right sort of relationship and information at hand, and access to suitable and adequate resources, assessment has the potential to play a key role in offering choice. However, there are problems as far as people like Jim and Marianne are concerned. We examine these now.

'Ordinarily resident'

Many of the duties and powers of local authorities to assess arise only in relation to those 'ordinarily resident' in the area (Roberts, 1996, p. 163). As Jim and Marianne moved into the area only a year or so earlier it might be argued that they were someone else's responsibility. This could lead to unseemly wrangles between the local authority where they now live and the local authority where they came from, and where

Marianne's family still live, as to who picks up the bill. Where two local authorities are in disagreement about 'ordinary residence' only the Secretary of State can finally decide. Jim and Marianne have no right in law to insist on staying in the area if they want or need community care services.

Backlog of cases

Jim and Marianne are likely to have to wait for a full assessment.

It is not uncommon to have to wait for up to six months for a specialist assessment by an occupational therapist. Without an assessment quite simple aids, such as bath boards or bath seats, are unavailable, which means that domiciliary staff, such as home care assistants, are unable to carry out their jobs (Hadley and Clough, 1996, p. 78).

In law, it is possible for users of community care services to make a formal complaint about failure to assess, or even take the matter to court through a process known as 'judicial review'. However, few people have the know-how or financial resources to make this right a reality, even if they have the energy.

Marianne did get an early assessment because she was 'bed-blocking' in hospital, and she was given priority so that her bed could be used by another patient. But for many new and existing users of services a full and comprehensive assessment may mean a long wait.

Lack of knowledge that an assessment is going on

There is evidence that when care managers undertake assessments, the people on the receiving end are unaware of the significance of the meeting. John Baldock and Clare Ungerson, who conducted research into the experiences of stroke victims (like Jim) who were assessed for community care services after leaving hospital, found that of their 32 respondents only two knew they had had an assessment, what it was for, and who their care manager was. The meetings which in the eyes of the multidisciplinary teams constituted assessments, and at which the users and their relatives were present, were not recognised as such. Consequently, any opportunity to raise questions or ask for services or specific forms of assistance was wasted. Only two new users successfully negotiated the system, and both of these had been employed in public services in the past (Baldock and Ungerson, 1994, Chapter 2).

In other words, the assessment process is a mystery to many of those involved in it.

An ongoing process?

A cursory examination of Jim and Marianne's history suggests that their 'needs' changed over time. While they were in the rehabilitation hostel, their needs were for gainful employment; on leaving hospital, their needs were far more basic – a home, money, help in adjusting to new physical limitations. To work properly, assessment needs to be ongoing, not a one-off event.

Resource constraints

A care manager is expected to bear in mind resource constraints when assembling a care package. Of course, these vary from place to place and time to time. But this is a very real headache when it comes to starting from scratch, as any care manager working with Jim and Marianne will have to do. To illustrate this, we'll consider their housing needs. Obviously, housing is a pressing need, without which little can be done. But the information on housing in the community care plan was, to say the least, sketchy. Now try your hand at listing the problems Jim, Marianne and their care manager are likely to face when it comes to housing, making use of information in Unit 6, Section 2.

Activity 7 | **Housing for Jim and Marianne**

Allow about 20 minutes

Re-read Unit 6, Section 2, then make a list of the problems you foresee in providing housing suited to Jim and Marianne's needs. Note any additional problems you can think of which are not mentioned there.

Comment | I noted the following:

- Most housing is designed for able-bodied people. There is likely to be a shortage of 'special needs housing'. I also noted that, because Jim and Marianne are disabled in different ways, the likelihood of finding housing suitable for both of them is even less.

- Most accommodation for people like Jim and Marianne is likely to be in specialist facilities where 'care' is also supplied. Jim and Marianne may not want this, as they have been accustomed to a good deal of freedom of movement. Also, would they be treated as a couple or would Marianne be offered a place in a hostel, leaving Jim to fend for himself on the streets?

- Housing needs are to be dealt with as part of a needs assessment, but most housing is the responsibility of housing departments. In Unit 6 it was noted that planning and communication between housing and social services departments are often poor. Teamworking will be essential if Jim and Marianne are to get a home that meets their physical needs.

An additional problem not mentioned in Unit 6 is that Jim and Marianne are likely to be seen as 'undeserving' compared with respectable citizens like Esther Hurdle, and may be at the bottom of any priority list.

Who provides housing for community care?

Housing associations
Housing associations are non-profit-distributing organisations run by voluntary committees. Some cater for general needs, others are more specialist. They are financed by housing association grants (HAGs) and special needs management allowances (SNMAs).

Local authorities
Local authorities own a decreasing amount of council housing for the general population and also provide sheltered accommodation – in 1996 16 per cent of total local authority housing stock. Some older sheltered housing is hard to let because accommodation with shared facilities, such as bathrooms, is unpopular with older people used to the comforts of their own homes.

NHS
The NHS has built residential units for patients being transferred from long-stay hospitals, especially disabled people, and people with long-term mental health problems.

In the light of this discussion of one important aspect of provision, we can say with some certainty that matching Jim and Marianne's needs to the available resources will be a major challenge to any care manager. Their own preferences are likely to come well down the list.

Community responses

Contrasting communities

As far as people like Jim and Marianne are concerned, a care manager is going to be aware of likely community responses to any decision to house former or continuing drug users in residential areas, as well as accusations that such people are less deserving than others needing care. Implicitly, if not explicitly, practitioners making arrangements for 'difficult' clients, such as drug users, are expected to take into account the well-being and rights of the community at large, as well as that of the individuals. You can see from the quotations given here that some are seen as more deserving of help than others:

> *Neighbours slam family from hell.*
>
> (Beds on Sunday, *27 April 1997)*

> *Putting girls into Council flats and providing tax payer funded child care is a policy from hell.*
>
> *(Stephen Green, Chairman, Conservative Family Campaign, 1993)*

> *I've got a little list of young ladies who get pregnant just to jump the housing list.*
>
> *(Peter Lilley, then Social Services Secretary, October 1992)*

Emotional adjustment

Becoming a new user of community care services, whoever you are, can be stressful. Remember what Marianne said just before leaving hospital: 'Look at me now. What a way to live. I wouldn't do it to a dog.' There will be a period of emotional adjustment to new roles, identities and physical or mental limitations. Here is what Baldock and Ungerson wrote about the responses of the people they interviewed to their new situations a few months after leaving hospital:

> *These later phases of emotional distress were a direct consequence of what we have called the 'unscripted nature of social dependency' ... They had returned home to find the legitimate normality of their lives undermined by their new disabilities ... they lead to changed relationships with other people, particularly close kin, and they lead to a new and often less confident and less powerful sense of identity ... Professionals necessarily focus primarily on tackling the more objective difficulties and know well the stubborn objections of people who, for example, refuse to be seen in a wheelchair, to accept moving the bed downstairs ... the objections are not to the practicality ... of the solutions but rather to the disturbance to the known and scripted routines of daily life, and the uncertainty about the appropriate new forms of behaviour and relationship.*
>
> *(Baldock and Ungerson, 1994, p. 46)*

If we think of the position of newcomers to community care in terms of learning new scripts to accompany their unwonted position of dependency, it becomes easier to understand why even copious quantities of written and verbal information and the best assessments of practical needs may not be enough to ease the transition.

3.4 Overcoming the barriers?

The chances of overcoming the barriers I have identified appear to be small. In Section 5 of this unit we spend more time on different strategies for change. But within the context of the community care system, can anything be done to improve practice? Some of the issues we have explored, such as shortage of resources, rules about residence and the response of the wider community, are not within an individual's power to change substantially. But some of the issues I have highlighted – provision of accessible information, awareness that an assessment is going on, and emotional responses – can be addressed by individual care managers. They will need to bear in mind that:

- most people will need a good deal of help if they are to be effective users of community care services
- assessments may be an everyday experience for workers – but they are often quite a new experience for service users
- people need information, but information alone is not enough

- relationships must take into account people's need for adjustment to new roles and relationships as well as their objective material needs

- if assessment is to be effective in meeting changing needs, then it has to be an ongoing process.

It is not only care managers who will have the opportunity to make use of the insights this section offers. All kinds of workers or volunteers come into contact with new users of community care, and an awareness of the issues involved as people take on new roles will help to improve practice.

This view offers practitioners a way of looking at the world that does not only blame resource constraints, but looks beyond those to consider how, even in a world where resources are not infinite (and they never are or will be), those who work in care services might do better if they have a little more understanding of the feelings and the difficulties of adjustment that new service users experience.

Key points

- Enabling users of services and their families to make choices was an aim of the community care reforms.

- Under the NHS and Community Care Act 1990 social services departments have a duty to publish an annually updated community care plan, one of whose purposes is to inform users of the range of services in their area.

- Community care assessments have the potential to play a key role in offering choice to users of community care services. However, there are many barriers to the exercise of choice. Help from practitioners to new users needs to incorporate a recognition that people need support in understanding their entitlements and adjusting to new situations. Assessment needs to be seen as an ongoing process.

Study skills: Keeping up your concentration

Do you feel you are settling into a rhythm of studying now? Are you managing to avoid the kind of bitty, distracted sessions you read about in the case of Michael, on pages 3 and 4 of *The Good Study Guide*? Have you got over the urge to make a cup of tea as soon as you have seated yourself, or to tidy your shelves? Of course, there are reasons why it is so easy to be distracted when you study – look back quickly at the box on page 10 of *The Good Study Guide*. You need to understand what helps you concentrate.

Think back over your best sessions of study. When have you concentrated particularly well? Was it when you:

- had set yourself a clear target?

- switched regularly from one task to another?

- made a point of scanning ahead so that you knew what you were reading about?

- were fresh from a nap?

- were really interested in the topic?

Or did other things keep you focused? You are the best person to work out what helps you concentrate. You need to take the time to try out different approaches and then reflect on what has been effective. But talking to other students can also be very helpful. When you hear about other people's study habits you begin to recognise where your own are distinctive. And sometimes you hear yourself explaining points about your ways of studying that you had never quite realised before. The more insight you have into your own motivation, capabilities and habits of thought, the better you can plan to play to your strengths. Don't feel you have to study according to some universal formula. There isn't one. Make up your own.

Section 4

Choice of services in the mixed economy of care

In Section 3 we considered how far users of services can exercise choice over their community care packages. If there is to be choice, then there has to be a variety of services to choose from for any particular need. This is what is meant by the 'mixed economy of care'. In this section we take a close look at issues for users in gaining access to services in a mixed economy.

4.1 Mapping the mixed economy

We discussed in Unit 3 how the community care reforms of 1990 introduced the idea of a mixed economy of care, with services provided from a number of different sources and purchased on behalf of the user by a care manager. The intention was to move from monopoly suppliers, where services were available only from state services, to a system that utilised the private, voluntary and informal sectors. It meant opening up the possibility that contributions could be made from 'the community' too. It would obviously be an over-simplification to suggest that before 1990 all services were supplied by the statutory sector of health and social services. You need only think of individuals, such as childminders, or long-established voluntary organisations, such as the Red Cross, the NSPCC and Barnardos, to realise that there has always been a variety of providers of social care. But, since the reforms, the variety of providers has increased dramatically, and the role of social services in providing services has correspondingly reduced. The example in the box below shows how one local authority diversified provision.

The mixed economy in Wandsworth

In 1997 the London Borough of Wandsworth had gone further than most in creating a mixed economy of care.

- Its six children's homes were run by Shaftesbury Homes and Arethusa, a voluntary organisation.

- Its old people's homes were run by housing associations and a private sector health care company.

- Its day care centres and luncheon clubs were run by local voluntary groups.

- Its meals on wheels were run by a private contractor.

- Its home care services were run by the council, which had won the contract in a tendering competition against other providers.

(*Adapted from Daniels, 1997, p. 4*)

However, the more providers of services there are, the more sophisticated people have to be if they are to make use of increased choice.

To illustrate the complexities of accessing the mixed economy we turn to Baldock and Ungerson, whose study I cited in Section 3. They interviewed 32 stroke victims who were new to community care services in East Kent in the early days of the community care reforms (1992–4). They found that in the early months of being users people had used a huge range of helping services. They grouped sources of help into five categories:

- kin (or relatives)
- privately purchased
- voluntary
- neighbours
- public sector.

I shall take just one of these categories, privately purchased care, to examine in detail. The box below summarises Baldock and Ungerson's findings on the sources of help their respondents made use of in the private sector.

Privately purchased care

1 Medical services, e.g. private hospital care*, private nursing home care*

2 Paramedical services:
(a) physiotherapy*
(b) chiropody*
(c) speech therapy*

3 Alternative therapies, e.g. homeopathy, osteopathy

4 Aids and adaptations:
(a) major aids, e.g. hoists, wheelchairs, stairlifts, lifts*
(b) minor aids, e.g. ramps, handrails*
(c) internal reorganisation of house, e.g. installation of shower/bath/lavatory
(d) alarm system*
(e) entry phone*

5 Private purchase of new accommodation suited to dependence

6   Use of private car to access care or make it more palatable
7   Social care
     (a)   private residential care: (1) permanent*, (2) respite*
     (b)   private day care*
     (c)   private home care, including personal care, on periodic basis*
     (d)   private domestic help, on periodic basis
     (e)   gardener, on periodic basis
     (f)   live-in housekeeper/companion.

* Forms of care for which there are direct substitutes available free or heavily subsidised in the pubic sector, but which are also in short supply in the public sector (at least in East Kent)

(Adapted from Baldock and Ungerson, 1994, p. 33)

You can see from the box that the services range from the sorts of thing almost anyone might purchase – a car, the services of a builder, a gardener, a new home – to quite specialised services, which they might need help from professionals or specialist information sources to access. This is especially the case for the medical services mentioned.

The information in the box suggests that people with money were at an advantage over people who were poor in making use of the private sector. Baldock and Ungerson's respondents identified possession of a car as being the single most important factor that promoted access and choice. If they had the use of a car, the stroke victims could use the services available to them selectively.

> *Mr. T, 87, decided to drive Mrs. T, 86, to the Day Hospital at times that would allow her to just use the parts of the service she wanted:*
>
> *Mr. T: They wanted to take her in the ambulance.*
>
> *Mrs. T: It's eight o'clock or something in the morning, and seven in the evening home!*
>
> *Mr. T: So I used to take her in every Wednesday morning about 10 o'clock, go off to Ashford Market, and then pick her up again on the way home.*
>
> *Mrs. T: It saved you all that terrible waiting in the afternoon for the ambulance. We'd done all the physiotherapy and the speech therapy. In the afternoons they used to make us do little things like tripping (sic) our hands up and down, you know, all very good, but everybody's thinking 'I've got things I could be doing at home'.*
>
> *(Baldock and Ungerson, 1994, p. 32)*

But there were other factors that enabled people to make use of sources of help, or hindered them. You'll see in the box that there are asterisks by the sorts of services that were also provided in the public sector. Some of Baldock and Ungerson's respondents feared that if they used these services it would prejudice their chances of getting the heavily subsidised or free help from the public sector if it became available. In Mr and Mrs E's view, the fact that they had employed a physiotherapist privately had put them at the back of the queue for the NHS-supplied service, and they believed it may have been seen as an implicit criticism of the NHS service (p. 29).

A further point to note from the information in the box is that only a minority of the private services listed here were things a care manager might be expected to suggest. Much of the research had been done by the users themselves, or their relatives, utilising their existing knowledge of local services, advice from friends, or directories such as Yellow Pages. People like Jim and Marianne, who are not members of settled communities, will be disadvantaged.

Baldock and Ungerson's study shows that a 'mixed economy' existed in East Kent in the early 1990s, with services available from a wide array of providers. In that sense it was a success story for the mixed economy. But not everyone was successful in gaining access to the range of choice on offer.

We go on to examine possible reasons for this.

4.2 Explaining user behaviour

In Unit 4 we discussed the idea that people follow the equivalent of scripts to enable them to play the wide variety of roles expected in daily life. We used the example of interactions between doctor and patient to show how powerful such scripts are in determining the way people present themselves, who asks the questions, and what sort of limits there are on the roles that can be adopted in such familiar situations. In Section 2 of this unit I referred to these doctor–patient interactions again. Indeed, Jim's account of the dusty reception they got at the hands of one or two primary care teams could be seen as a failure on their parts to play the right sort of patient role, through being scruffy or dirty, or arriving at the wrong time for surgery, or making inappropriate demands of the person they were speaking to.

Baldock and Ungerson's research suggested that a way of understanding some of the problems experienced by users of community care services is that they are suddenly being required to play new roles to new scripts, and no one has told them the lines. In Section 3 I quoted their findings that new users have a considerable emotional adjustment to make when they find themselves in the unwonted position of being 'dependent'. Baldock and Ungerson suggest that the change to a mixed economy can exacerbate people's difficulties of adjustment. They argue that:

- People for the most part did not expect care services to be obtained on the open market; they were used to being told what to do.

- This sort of mixed economy was unlike the retail market of shops and mail order. In the mixed economy of care some services were free, some were charged for, some could be bought on the open market, some not, and some were available from a variety of sources.

To assist in understanding people's behaviour they created a model which places users of community care into four ideal types. You will find it described in Chapter 29 of the Reader.

Activity 8 **Describing the model**

Allow about 30 minutes   Read Chapter 29 of the Reader, 'Becoming consumers of community care'. Then make your own notes on the four types of user described.

Comment   You'll see that the model sets up four types of user:

Consumers – who expect nothing from the state and set out to arrange care by buying it, just as they might buy a new car, or any other kind of consumer goods. They believe that using the market in this way gives them more control and autonomy than using state services, even if they are free.

Privatists – who focus their lives on their homes, and who find dependence hard to adjust to because it often means asking for help. The market does not meet all their needs, and they tend to become isolated.

Welfarists – who expect and demand their rights to welfare services as citizens, and have the know-how and energy to get the best out of the public and voluntary services.

Clientists – who rather passively accept what they are offered, without either demanding more or expecting that the services will respond to their needs in anything but a rigid, prescribed way.

Like all models, this is a representation of reality – no one fell exactly into any one category. Nevertheless, it can be a helpful way to think about the range of scripts available to new users.

Activity 9   **Applying the model**

Allow about 20 minutes   Using what you have learnt from Chapter 29 of the Reader, answer the following questions:

(a)   Jim and Marianne are, as I have noted, unlike the people interviewed by Baldock and Ungerson. Which, if any, of the four categories do you think best represents their likely script, and why?

(b)   Where in the model would you place:
  •   the Durrants (Block 1)
  •   the Brights (Block 2)
  •   the arguments in favour of independent living (Unit 3).

Comment (a) Judging from what has been said about Jim and Marianne in this unit so far, it seems likely they will adopt either the welfarist or the clientist scripts. They do not have the money to be privatists, and their history of being consumers is weak. Since they already have some know-how from earlier in their lives, for example in locating sympathetic GPs, they might have the energy and inside knowledge to actively pursue their entitlements (welfarism); but, as Marianne said, when they are not feeling too good about themselves, the sort of passive acceptance of what is offered that characterises clientism seems likely. An alternative is that they will drop out of the system and return to the streets – which is perhaps a form of self-defeating privatism.

(b) The Durrants fit most easily into the clientist script. They do not appear to have the knowledge or resources to fight effectively for flexible services to meet their needs, and lack of cash means they cannot utilise the private sector, except via the care manager.

Mrs Bright's energetic pursuit of extra services when she needs them places her more in a welfarist script.

The arguments in favour of independent living seem to fall between welfarism (in the sense of actively pursuing entitlements using rights-based arguments) and consumerism (arranging care on the open market).

Models, as Baldock and Ungerson say in the Reader, are only a crude method of representing the different ways people respond to new situations. The model they presented was drawn from only one group in one area of the country. A similar project investigating a different group – say drug users – or in a different part of the UK might throw up different lists and different models. But models *are* useful in helping to make sense of complex situations. You will be using this one again in Unit 11.

4.3 From welfare state to mixed economy

 I have suggested that, as the philosophy of care provision moved from the expectations set up by the post-1945 welfare state, of care from cradle to grave, to a system in which 'market', 'consumer choice', 'competition' and 'mixed economy' were the watchwords, if users were to be 'successful' they had to adapt their behaviour to make the best use of the new environment. Baldock and Ungerson's research shows that some people (consumers and welfarists) – those with most private resources, confidence and knowledge – can make good use of the opportunities offered in a mixed economy. But those who are impoverished, have few community networks, are very frail or confused, or who are perceived as 'difficult', appear to find it hard to take advantage of the opportunities for choice, and may have been better served by the promises of universal equitable care for all which characterised the mid-twentieth-century welfare state.

You have seen throughout this unit that 'difficult' or 'disadvantaged' people experience considerable barriers in gaining access to health and social care services in the community, and that even when they do access such services, their opportunities to make choices are limited. In the final section of this unit we explore some strategies that have been advocated to promote access to services designed to benefit everyone, but especially those most disadvantaged.

Key points

- The 'mixed economy' of care was ushered in by the NHS and Community Care Act 1990. It refers to the existence of a variety of providers of care and support – from private, voluntary and statutory services to neighbourhood networks and the support of relatives and friends – and is intended to promote choice by users of services.

- The mixed economy exists in some areas and for some services.

- Many users find it hard to access the benefits of the mixed economy partly because they are poor, frail or have little or no access to information and resources; and partly because the system is hard to comprehend.

Section 5
Strategies for change

This unit has spent some time exploring barriers to accessing a variety of community services – primary care, community care and housing. I have noted how far Jim and Marianne, and individuals like them who are seen as 'difficult', 'deviant' or just plain expensive, are disadvantaged when it comes to getting the services to which they are theoretically entitled, so much so that it may be tempting for them just to throw in the towel and give up. And you have seen that, although individual practitioners, GPs and care managers can have some impact, what they can achieve as individuals is limited both by resources and by the system.

Now it is time to consider what might be done to improve matters, what strategies for change exist and how far they might improve access for the likes of Jim and Marianne.

5.1 Charters: creating better consumers

In Section 2 reference was made to the rights of patients to GP services enshrined in the Patient's Charter, produced by the Department of Health. Charters can be seen as a way of making people better *consumers* by informing them of their rights. Some charters go further than the Patient's Charter.

The box below shows a charter of rights for drug users drawn up by SCODA (the Standing Conference on Drug Abuse). Unlike the Patient's Charter, this does not have the backing of central government. It can be seen as a set of aspirations, and has the advantage of being a users'-eye view of what people should have a right to demand.

Drug Users' Charter

Drug users have the right to:

- assessment of individual need within a specified number of days

- specialist services within a specified maximum waiting time

- respect for privacy, dignity and confidentiality

- a complaints procedure

- full information about treatment and informed involvement in making decisions about treatment

- a second opinion when referred to a consultant

- an individual care and treatment plan

- immediate access to treatment programmes on release from prison

- information about self help groups and drug user rights groups.

(Standing Conference on Drug Abuse, 1997, p. 3)

The Drug Users' Charter

Using the Drug Users' Charter, make your own notes in answer to the
following questions:

(a)   Who do you think might make use of such a charter – and when?

(b)   How do you think a service provider might react if presented with
such a charter?

Comment   (a)   Inevitably, I thought of Jim and Marianne as likely users of such a
charter. They might use it when meeting a GP who was resistant to
accepting them, or maybe when they wanted a particular treatment or
course of action which was being denied.

(b)   I found it hard to think of a practitioner reacting positively, and
imagined many viewing such an action as a condemnation of the
treatment that was being offered.

On reflection, I could see the charter as useful to have as a last
resort, if it was impossible to get satisfaction by any other means.

Charters do give users an idea of their rights but, as the activity shows,
it is difficult to see how they can be used routinely. The rights are often
couched in general terms, and hard to translate into action. Charters do
not mean that there are more resources, just that some people (perhaps
the sorts who are successful welfarists) may be better able to access
what there is. As a strategy for change, unless ways can be found of
providing the kinds of service drug users need and persuading agencies
that they should adopt these as aspirations, charters have limited use.

5.2 Advocacy

What is advocacy? An advocate is defined by Ken Simons as an
'unconditional ally for an individual who is vulnerable; someone to be
on the side of their partner' (Simons, 1993, p. 14). The principles of
advocacy may be applicable to anyone whose rights and wishes are
ignored or overruled. There are numerous types of advocacy, ranging
from agencies such as welfare rights organisations, to legal ombudsmen,
professionals and workers whose role includes acting as an advocate for
their patients or clients, to unpaid individuals who choose to take on the
role.

There are many ways in which an advocate might work with Jim and
Marianne.

•   They might speak up for them at the doctors' surgery or at other
agencies they will have to come into contact with, or encourage
them to speak up for themselves.

•   They might provide practical help with budgeting and sorting out
domestic or housing matters.

•   They might give advice and information on benefits, other agencies
from which Jim and Marianne might get support, and so on.

•   They might also offer friendship and help to re-establish a sense of
self-worth for Jim and Marianne.

But who might be an advocate? Two types of advocacy are:

•   *Paid professionals* acting as advocates as a part of the job.

•   *Unpaid citizens* who take on the role as volunteers. Jim mentioned
being an advocate himself when he worked briefly in the

rehabilitation centre. At that time he describes going with other clients to visit their doctors' surgeries. Advocates can be family or friends, but the role can also be formalised through peer or citizen advocacy schemes. Such advocates enter into an independent, voluntary relationship with a person who needs someone to help them defend or exercise their rights, and to gain acceptance into the life of the community (Citizen Advocacy Information and Training, 1996).

There are advantages and disadvantages to both types of advocacy – paid professionals or workers acting for their patients/clients, and volunteers. Think this through by doing the next activity.

Activity 11 **Advocates for Jim and Marianne?**

Allow about 10 minutes Answer the following questions briefly.

(a) If Jim and Marianne's GP decided to act as an advocate for them, what might he be able to offer? What factors might limit his effectiveness as an advocate? (It will help if you consider the issues raised in the discussion of Chapter 5 in the Reader, in Section 1.)

(b) If you were a trained volunteer citizen advocate, what might you be able to offer? What might limit your effectiveness?

Comment (a) As a local health professional a GP could offer a knowledge of what might be available, and might be able to exert pressure to ensure that Jim and Marianne were accepted into a suitable service. But his professional code of conduct might mean he was obliged to report on any illegal activities. If they had had children he might not have been able to act as their unconditional ally. In addition, he might need to consider the likely reactions of colleagues and others if he seemed to be favouring one couple over other patients. He would also need to be prepared to be self-critical, and recognise that he may be part of the problem!

(b) Most course testers observed that as a citizen advocate they would have fewer conflicts of role to consider than a paid professional acting as an advocate. One commented:

'At least I could be quite single-minded, and would not need to worry about other patients.'

However, others sounded a note of caution:

'I'm not sure I'd want to be involved if it meant turning a blind eye to illegal activities like dealing in drugs.'

'Where do you start? At least a worker knows the system. I'd be starting from scratch.'

'I'd be wondering if I wanted to take on an open-ended commitment. I might not even like them.'

'How would I find them when I wanted to speak to them? They haven't even got a phone number.'

In advocacy there is a balance to consider between independence and absence of role conflict (most likely to be found in volunteers) and the advantages of local know-how, which are most likely to lie with community-based workers.

Both strategies, charters and advocacy, appear to have the potential to help Marianne and Jim to some extent. We have seen that neither strategy is without its problems, but taken together there is hope for change. Without an advocate or ally, they may not be successful in putting their charter rights into operation. But the sort of statement of rights or aspirations that charters provide can be a starting point for an advocate who might volunteer to work with Jim and Marianne.

One criticism that can be levelled at such individualistic strategies is that they may advantage some people – make them into more successful consumers – but when resources are limited others who do not have these advantages may lose out.

The next two strategies for change we examine aim at the community at large, rather than at particular individuals.

5.3 Community outreach

'Outreach' is the term used to describe activities that seek to reach people who are not making use of services they need. You have seen that homeless people and drug users who want treatment often find it hard to come by health and care services. Judgemental attitudes combined with competition for limited resources mean that many are deterred, despite the rights they have under the Patient's Charter. The consequences can be dire for the individual, and costly for health and care services when individuals become as ill as were Jim and Marianne when they entered hospital. A strategy to bridge the gap is community outreach.

In a rural area of north-east Essex drug users themselves were recruited and trained as outreach volunteers. They were given the task of contacting drug users and assisting them in practices to reduce harm, such as using sterile syringes, advising on drug services locally and providing information on safer sex. Building on existing networks, the drug user volunteers made a considerable impact. They knew where drug users met, and were able to incorporate their work as volunteers in their daily lives. Results from a survey of the scheme (Boulton and Walling, 1993, p. 15) show that:

- 46 of 66 respondents had heard of the scheme

- 34 (over 50 per cent) were in regular contact with a volunteer

- 23 of those 34 who were in contact with a volunteer were not in contact with any other drug service

- the informal syringe exchange service established by volunteers had made an impact – there was less sharing of syringes

- the volunteers themselves experienced increased self-esteem and social standing.

The authors of the report on the north-east Essex scheme believe that the use of drug users as volunteers brought considerable benefits. However, monitoring the scheme proved impossible because, as they write:

> *Volunteers do not want to keep records or report to someone on what they do ... Volunteers who were being most successful in drugs outreach were the ones most opposed to monitoring.*
>
> (Boulton and Walling, 1993, p. 15)

Lack of monitoring means that drug use is still poorly documented or understood, and it is hard to make a strong case for more funding or better services. The illegality of drug use means that arguing for more services is dubious anyway.

Community outreach is a strategy that is applicable to groups other than drug users. Homeless people are another group that is hard to reach, as are some members of minority ethnic groups who may be unaware of the sorts of service they can expect, or be deterred by the expectation that they will meet prejudice, or be offered services that simply do not meet their needs.

One drawback is that successful outreach may well stimulate a demand for services which are non-existent or already at full stretch. If the north-east Essex scheme had prompted drug users to come forward for rehabilitation, could the existing services have responded? Giles Woolford's family spent a year badgering for a place in a detoxification centre when he decided he wanted to break the hold heroin had over him. In the end he got two weeks in hospital – not enough to prevent his sliding back into addiction within a month (Bosely, 1997, p. 2). Like charters and advocacy, outreach is a strategy that can make a difference, but without more and better services, the impact will be limited.

5.4 Experimental health centres

We have looked at making services more accessible through various strategies – charters, advocacy, community outreach. It is probably unrealistic to expect that drug addicts, perceived to be among the least deserving of the thousands of people in competition for scarce resources, should ever expect to have as much as they may need to break them of their addiction, and support them in the difficult adjustment to life after drugs. An alternative strategy is to create services that have a broad vision of serving the health of the whole community.

The Peckham Experiment

You might like to write this on to the wallchart

Within primary care, developments are taking place that are evidence of changed ways of thinking about health and that acknowledge the influence of social, economic and environmental factors in the health of individual people and the communities in which they live. Many of these new initiatives have adopted the thinking behind the 'Peckham Experiment'. In 1926, the Peckham Experiment was initiated, based on an innovative health centre which would provide a range of social, recreational and fitness activities for local people. The aim was to foster 'positive health' and 'to create the right conditions for the emergence of health rather than just the treatment of disease'. The Pioneer Health Centre opened in 1935 and included a swimming pool, gym, badminton courts, games rooms, playground, nursery, cafeteria and dance hall. The biologists who established the project believed that, given the opportunity, individuals and families would choose healthy options. Their core principles included:

- *an orientation towards health, interpreted in a broad, holistic way*
- *member participation and self determination*
- *multi-generational membership*
- *a range of opportunities/integrated activities.*

(Gaskin and Vincent, 1996a, p. 14)

The Peckham Experiment

Below is a description of what the Peckham Experiment offered to local people:

> *Here was an environment for the chance meeting; but also, and more important, for continual and repeated meetings, and so for acquaintanceship, companionship and developing friendships ...*
> *Everything taking place there was carried on by people who, belonging to the locality and continuously using the Centre, came to be known personally to each other through sharing in some of the many facilities of the Centre life; or through the day to day doings of their children; or merely known by sight as members participating in a common experience.*

> *(Pioneer Health Centre, 1971, p. 4)*

More recent innovations have followed many of these principles (Scott-Samuel, 1990) and a recent report evaluating the effectiveness of co-operative, socially based, primary care initiatives concludes:

> *Evidence suggests that we are at a landmark stage in the evolution of thinking about health. So many different elements appear to be coming together and culminating in a qualitative shift in the culture of health care delivery and health promotion. This challenges our social and political system to respond with creative and effective new forms. On the evidence so far, the models of community well-being centres and co-operative structures offer exciting new ways of realising the potential of people and communities to improve the overall health of the nation as we move into the 21st Century.*

> *(Gaskin and Vincent, 1996b, p. 76)*

How far such approaches might embrace the issues that confront Jim and Marianne is doubtful. Setting aside the illegal nature of their habit, which such a place is unlikely to countenance, the Peckham Centre was locality based – and Jim and Marianne have little to connect them to where they happen to live. It is indeed hard to imagine 'the community' embracing transient outcasts like them. Or could *they* change, given the opportunity to enjoy a healthier lifestyle?

5.5 Reviewing strategies for change

The strategies to improve access to services discussed in this section are wide-ranging, sometimes idealistic, sometimes exciting. They all offer potential. None can be seen as a straightforward blueprint for addressing the problems faced by Jim and Marianne, our reference point so far, but they are well worth consideration when thinking about the broad topic of this unit, access to health and social care.

Conclusion

In this unit you have been considering questions of access to community services. The nature of community as it is traditionally seen, as membership of a place with its accompanying networks and facilities, seems to exclude Jim and Marianne, and people like them. Jim and Marianne are people on the margins of community as it is usually conceived. They have very few of the attributes that confer membership of local communities – no home, no jobs, very little money, few local networks, little respect or self-confidence. Because most health and social care services assume that people who come to them will have some kind of community base, at the very least a home, they are at an immediate disadvantage when it comes to access. The disadvantages do not stop there. They face discrimination. Even if the individual practitioner is open-minded and welcoming, there lurk shadows – what will other people think, is there a threat to the welfare of others, what right do such people have to what is always a limited amount of resources, where is the line to be drawn between deserving and undeserving cases? In comparison with other user groups – disabled people and children in care, for example – drug users and homeless people command little public sympathy or support.

On the positive side, looking at the person behind the label can begin to redress the balance so that even the most disadvantaged and difficult people emerge as human beings whose problems, if they cannot be solved, can be understood and empathised with. Services at the very least aspire to be open to all who need them. And there is a range of strategies that can be explored as means to make the ideal of access for all more of a reality.

What general lessons can be learnt about access to community services from your study in this unit? Three points stand out.

1   If the intention is to maximise access it is not enough to place a service geographically within a community and publicise its existence. It is not even enough to undertake an individual needs assessment.

2   Services need to be fitted to people, rather than people being expected to fit in with services. They need to adapt to different kinds of user and potential user, and remain alert to who is left out.

3   Many mainstream services assume that users will have a home and be part of a geographical community. Some people have neither.

If you have time, make your own links from the conclusion to this unit to the core questions now, just to make sure you have grasped the main ideas. The core questions were:

• What barriers are there to access to community health and care services?

• To what extent can people exercise choice in the services they access?

• What strategies exist to promote access to services for people who are disadvantaged?

Study skills: Granting yourself the time

I talked earlier about the little distractions that can so easily disturb your studies. But what about more urgent distractions – worries about untouched housework, pressures at work, getting the WC repaired, keeping the children from self-destruction? Are you feeling guilty right now about what you have failed to achieve outside your studies, as well as your shortcomings within the course? Is this whole study thing a bad idea?

How can you balance all the demands from outside K100 against your own need for personal development through study? You need to think about the priorities in your life. Some things just won't get done – or will not be done as thoroughly as before you were studying. But are you giving more time to K100 than you can really afford? Or are there other things you need to drop, to take some of the pressure off? Do you need to talk to family or friends to explain the demands on your time?

Now that you have two months' experience of K100 you need to be looking for a balance in your life as an independent student. You need to weigh up what is important so that you can grant yourself a suitable amount of study time. The worst of all worlds is to find yourself wasting hard-won study time while worrying about what you are not doing elsewhere.

References

Association of Community Health Councils for England and Wales (1994) *Patients' Rights*, Association of Community Health Councils for England and Wales, London.

Audit Commission (1996) *What the Doctor Ordered*, HMSO, London.

Baldock, J. and Ungerson, C. (1994) *Becoming Consumers of Community Care*, Joseph Rowntree Foundation, York.

Boulton, K. and Walling, A. (1993) 'User to user', *Druglink*, July/August, pp. 14–15.

Bosely, S. (1997) 'When love isn't enough', *Guardian*, 21 April.

Citizen Advocacy Information and Training (1996) *CAIT Information*, CAIT, London.

Daniels, A. (1997) '"No essential reason" to insist on in-house services', *Guardian*, 13 March, p. 4.

Davies, A. and Huxley, P. (1997) 'Survey of general practitioners' opinions on treatment of opiate users', *British Medical Journal*, Vol. 314, 19 April, pp. 1173–74.

Department of Health (1989a) *An Introduction to the Children Act 1989*, HMSO, London.

Department of Health (1989b) *Caring for People*, Cm 849, HMSO, London.

Department of Health (1996) *Primary Care: Delivering the Future*, Cm 3511, HMSO, London.

Franks, P., Clancy, C. and Nutting, P. (1992) 'Gatekeeping revisited – protecting patients from overtreatment', *New England Journal of Medicine*, Vol. 327, pp. 424–9.

Gaskin, K. and Vincent, J. (1996a) 'Peckham principles and co-operation in community well-being schemes', *Purchasing in Practice*, Vol. 10, pp. 14–15.

Gaskin, K. and Vincent, J. (1996b) *Co-operating for Health: The Potential of the Co-operative Movement and Community Well-being Centres to Health of the Nation Activities*, Centre for Research in Social Policy, Loughborough University, Loughborough.

Greenwood, J. (1992) 'Persuading general practitioners to prescribe – good husbandry or a recipe for chaos?' *British Journal of Addiction*, Vol. 87, pp. 567–74.

Hadley, R. and Clough, R. (1996) *Care in Chaos*, Cassell, London.

Kidd, B. and Stark, C. (1995) *Management of Violence and Aggression in Health Care*, Gaskell/Royal College of Psychiatrists, London.

Leaver, E.J., Elford, J., Morris, J.K. and Cohen, J. (1992) 'Use of general practice by intravenous heroin users on a methadone programme', *British Journal of General Practice*, Vol. 42, pp. 465–8.

McKeganey, N. (1988) 'Shadowland: general practitioners and the treatment of opiate abusing patients', *British Journal of Addiction*, Vol. 83, pp. 373–86.

North, C., Moore, H. and Owens, C. (1996) *Go Home and Rest?*, Shelter, London.

Pioneer Health Centre (1971) *The Peckham Experiment*, Pioneer Health Centre, London.

Roberts, G. (1996) 'Empowerment and community care: some of the legal issues', in Ramcharan, P., Roberts, G., Grant, G. and Borland, J. (eds) *Empowerment in Everyday Life: Learning Disability*, Jessica Kingsley, London.

Scott-Samuel, A. (ed.) (1990) *Total Participation, Total Health; Re-inventing the Peckham Health Centre for the 1990s*, Scottish Academic Press, Edinburgh.

Simons, K. (1993) *Citizen Advocacy: The Inside View*, Norah Fry Research Centre, Bristol.

Social Services Inspectorate/Scottish Social Work Group (1991) *Care Management and Assessment. Manager's Guide*, HMSO, London.

Standing Conference on Drug Abuse (1997) *Getting Drug Users Involved*, SCODA, London.

Starfield, B. (1994) 'Is primary care essential?', *The Lancet,* Vol. 344, pp. 1129–33.

Starfield, B. (1995) 'Is strong primary care good for health outcomes?', lecture prepared for conference on the Future of Primary Care, Office of Health Economics, London, 13 September 1995.

Welsh, I. (1993) *Trainspotting*, Minerva, London.

Acknowledgements

Grateful acknowledgement is made to the following sources for permission to reproduce material in this unit:

Text

p. 30: Sheffield Community Care Services – Service Charter, Sheffield City Council, with permission; *pp. 35, 39–40*: Baldock, J. and Ungerson, C. (1994) *Becoming Consumers of Community Care: Households Within the Mixed Economy of Welfare*, Joseph Rowntree Foundation.

Illustrations

p. 8: Christopher Jones; *pp. 16, 19*: Paul Schatzberger; *pp. 20, 22*: © Crown Copyright 1983; *p. 25*: Socialist Health Association; *p. 34 (left)*: R.G. Richards; *p. 39*: Courtesy of Ashbourne plc; *p. 50*: Hulton Getty.

Unit 11
Caring Communities: Fact or Fiction?

Prepared for the course team by Martin Robb with Celia Davies

While you are working on Unit 11, you will need:
- Course Reader
- Offprints Book
- *The Good Study Guide*
- Audio Cassette 3, side 1
- Wallchart

Contents

Introduction

Health and social care services are designed to serve those who live in a particular geographical area. Such services are often described as being 'community-based'. But just how important is this term 'community'? Does it matter if some geographical areas are not communities in any clear sense, or if some people do not feel they belong to communities? Certainly it seemed to matter for Jim and Marianne in Unit 10. In this unit we will examine the whole notion of community more closely. We will consider what community means to different people, how uses of the term differ, and how far communities have changed. Where change has occurred, we will ask what factors have prompted it. We will ask whether some of the close-knit communities of the past were actually as ideal as some modern commentators seem to suppose that they were. None of this is to look at communities just for their own sake. We need to focus on communities in this more detailed way in order to understand what changes in communities, and diversity in ways of living, mean for the ability to care and be cared for. We will also ask why, from community nurses to community social workers, and community health trusts to community schools, and of course community care, the word 'community' appears to be everywhere.

We shall be looking for answers to four core questions.

Core questions

- What do people mean when they talk of community?
- How has people's experience of community changed in recent years?
- What is the relationship between 'community' and 'care'?
- What does working with communities involve?

Section 1
The many meanings of community

Community, you will quickly find out as you study the first two
sections of this unit, is an overworked term. There are almost as many
definitions of community as there are people doing the defining.
Furthermore, the word itself pops up in many different contexts,
meaning different things – and things that are not always spelled out
clearly. But to begin, you are asked to think about communities as places
for living in.

Activity 1   **Where do you live?**

Allow about 5 minutes   Most people faced with the question 'Where do you live?' will name a city,
a town or a village. Depending on who is doing the asking, and what the
questioner is likely to know about the locality, they may be more or less
precise, naming a district or even a street. But suppose that you were
asked whether you felt you lived now – or had ever lived – in a real, local
community, what would your immediate response be? Can you pinpoint
why you respond in the way you do?

Comment   There are many different answers that you might give to the question of
whether you live in a community now. They are likely to be affected by
whether you are in a city or in the country, whether you have made many
geographical moves in your lifetime, whether you are someone who is
home-based or out at work away from your area of residence during the
day, what local facilities and opportunities for meeting there are, and so on.
These are the sorts of factor that determine whether you actually know the
people who live around you, whether you feel that you have something in
common with them and whether you feel you belong. *Familiarity, shared
thinking* and a *sense of belonging* are some of the things you might have
singled out as what living in a community means.

Some of our course testers – especially the older ones among them – said
that they felt they had lived in a community in their childhood, although
not all of them did now. This feeling of having seen change, accompanied
by a belief in the decline of communities, is a powerful and important idea
and one that will be a theme of the unit as it develops.

To help you to think rather more about places as communities – with
characteristics such as 'familiarity', 'shared thinking' and 'a sense of
belonging', as were singled out above – and what this means for
people's daily lives and for the care they offer each other, we will step
back into the past. I will not, as you might expect, take you back to
village life in the countryside of 100 years ago, but instead take you into
the heart of London in the 1950s.

A community – or just somewhere to live?

1.1 A London working-class community in the 1950s

Bethnal Green is a compact and densely populated area in the East End of London. In the mid-1950s its population was about 54,000. The overwhelming majority of the men of Bethnal Green at this time were manual workers, many of them unskilled. The white-collar and professional classes who worked in the area – the teachers, doctors, local government officers, welfare workers – lived elsewhere. Men in Bethnal Green were market porters and dockers, skilled and unskilled workers in an array of small-scale industries such as boot and shoe making, tailoring and the furniture trade; the last of these was of particular importance in the area. Although it did not protect men from unemployment and their families from poverty and hardship, the very diversity of local industries meant that people in Bethnal Green, unlike those living in areas that were dependent on a single industry, had more chance of staying in the area if a particular industry collapsed, rather than having to move out of it in search of work. As you will see a little later, the wives of these men could go out to work to help make ends meet because mothers (or, less frequently, mothers-in-law) living close by were often able to care for children.

Areas within 1950s Bethnal Green were clearly marked off from each other. Bow was one such area, full of neat, small, privately rented houses with their polished doorknobs and whitened front steps. Here the men, often council employees, were in stable but poorly paid employment. The old weavers' cottages in the Bethnal Green Road area, where the houses and workshops of the cabinet makers, boot makers and tailors were intermingled, formed another area. Before the Second World War it had been more clearly divided into Jewish and Gentile streets – in the 1950s it was more mixed. Brick Lane and the Boundary Street Estate constituted a third distinct area, populated by people rehoused by the London County Council whom the locals saw as newcomers and foreigners.

This picture of a working-class area in London just over a generation ago emerges from what has been dubbed 'the Bethnal Green trilogy', a set of now classic studies of the nature of family and neighbourhood life by sociologists (who were still writing 40 years later on the theme of communities and about policies for care).

*   Peter Townsend (whom you have already encountered in Block 2 in relation to his later, influential work on institutions) carried out a study of the life of old people in the area (Townsend, 1957).

*   Michael Young and Peter Willmott studied couples with young families and compared their lives with those of people who had been relocated from Bethnal Green to a new housing estate in Essex. They traced what happened when people were cut off from long-standing contacts with family and friends (Young and Willmott, 1962; first published in 1957).

*   These two writers then followed this with an examination of the more affluent and middle-class area of Woodford (Willmott and Young, 1960).

Your reading for this section comes from what is probably the most well-known book in the trilogy – *Family and Kinship in East London*, first published in 1957. All the quotations, however, come from the revised edition, made available in paperback for a wide general readership five years later (Young and Willmott, 1962).

Before turning to the reading, you need a little more information about the study itself. Conducted between 1953 and 1955, it involved drawing a sample of every 36th name on the electoral register, and carrying out a brief interview with over 900 people, noting such details as age, employment and family composition. This was then followed by more detailed interviews with a smaller number of husbands and wives. Forty-five couples with two or more children under 15 were interviewed (sometimes separately, sometimes together) to find out more about their daily lives. The most striking finding was the extent to which the wider family – the parents of the couples they interviewed, brothers, sisters and cousins – lived in the area and were in close and

The Bethnal Green 'trilogy': classic studies of family and community

regular contact. 'We were surprised to discover', the authors comment in the introduction, 'that the wider family, far from having disappeared, was still very much alive in the middle of London' (Young and Willmott, 1962, p. 12). We pick up the story after these close relationships between kin have been documented. The authors then ask whether there is any room for a community beyond the family – whether neighbours and friends living close by were part of the lives of those whom they interviewed. The answer, as you will see, is a resounding 'yes'.

Study skills: Finding out about our society

We learn a lot about society through news reports and documentaries. Reporters go to places to talk to those involved in events, to passers-by on the street and to people in authority. But how far can we rely on accounts like these to give us an accurate picture of our society? Are the people interviewed doing much more than simply passing on impressions that other people have passed to them – especially when their views are compressed into 'sound bites'? And when we see people give contrasting accounts, how can we know which of them, if any, are typical of the population at large? Vital though such reports are in giving us regular 'spot checks' on the social climate, we need more systematically gathered information if we want to chart the main currents of change in society. For example, we read and hear a lot about what is happening to communities in our society. But news reporters are looking for 'stories', so perhaps we only learn about communities in trouble. Do the majority of people live in grim, terrorised streets, or only a few? Were there actually as many problems in the 'slums' of the past? Is it just that we have more vivid and wide-ranging reporting now, with cameras and microphones probing into all corners of society?

 Young and Willmott's study of Bethnal Green is an example of systematic sociological research, as opposed to news reporting. They limited the study to a specifically defined geographic area (rather than casting about in lots of places) and carefully selected a sample of 900 people for interview. Why did they decide on such a large sample, rather than one of, say, 20 people? Well, one group of 20 people may happen to contain five newcomers to the area, while another group of 20 may have none. When you have a bigger sample size, though, such variations tend to even out. (Look at the box on sampling errors on page 94 of *The Good Study Guide*.) An overall picture of the population of Bethnal Green could be established from this large sample. However, it would be expensive to interview so many people in depth, so a 10 per cent sample was drawn from the main sample (45 couples – i.e. 90 people). But this sample deliberately excluded single people and couples without children, or with one child, or children over 15. So it was no longer representative of the population at large. It is a sample that tells us only about families with young children. As you know from the charts in Units 1 and 6, this leaves out a lot of people.

As you study, you need to become aware of the difference between impressions of the world we form from the news media and the information provided by more detailed systematic studies. It is also important to take notice of sizes of samples and how they have been selected, so that you know how much confidence you can place in the conclusions drawn. Research findings don't always agree. You need to develop an ability to judge the quality of research in order to pick your way through the various studies you read.

Activity 2   Bethnal Green in the 1950s – a traditional community?

Allow about 30 minutes

Find Offprint 15 by Young and Willmott in the Offprints Book. Before you start to read it, jot down these three questions, leaving yourself plenty of room to make notes under each heading:

(a) What are the factors (according to Young and Willmott) that give Bethnal Green a 'sense of community'?

(b) How, in their view, is this community being sustained – what (and who) is keeping it the way it is?

(c) What are the negative aspects that emerge about living in Bethnal Green?

The authors provide a very vivid and enjoyable account of life in the area – you may find you want to read it like a novel, just for the story! Do not forget to come back to the questions. They are designed to help you tease out what is entailed in traditional ideas about community and begin to evaluate them.

Comment   (a)   Young and Willmott start by stressing the importance of *long residence* in the same area. They point out how very familiar people are with each other – they grew up together, they went to school and sometimes to work together. In a particularly important sentence that you may have highlighted, they say: 'Long residence by itself does something to create a sense of community with other people in the district'. Relatives are clearly very important to people in this community. Relatives act not as a barrier but as a bridge to the wider community, enlarging the range of contacts. Alongside this, a strong sense of attachment to the local area comes through. People know about its history; they do not travel far; they celebrate anniversaries and events together. There are also hints of support – in the shopping trip, for example, Mrs Landon tells how her mother had agreed to 'keep an eye on Mavis' when her own mother died and how Mavis 'pops in at Mum's every day'. Mrs Landon also says of another woman, Katie Simmons, 'She's from the turning. Mum nursed her Mum when she was having Katie.'

(b)   As far as the extract you have read is concerned, *long residence* in the area and the *presence of kin* repeatedly come through as factors keeping the community together. But what lies behind this? What, in other words, enabled people to stay in the area in the way that they did? You might have thought about the *availability of jobs* – I mentioned in the introduction to this section that men did not have to move in search of work in the way they had to in other areas. You might have thought about the *availability of housing*. Elsewhere in the book, the authors say a lot about how housing was allocated in a private rental market – a mother would speak to the rent collector when her newly married daughter needed a house and all kinds of complicated reciprocal arrangements would be put in train to enable families to move closer together. As to the question of who is sustaining all this, the answer seems to be that it is the women more than the men. It is a woman's shopping trip that forms the heart of the chapter and women's networks that emerge more clearly. The men remain more shadowy. (Did you notice that the wife of one of the authors collected this information? Phyllis Willmott went on to write an important guide to social services (1967). If your experience is in social work, you might also recognise her as the biographer of Geraldine Aves, a key figure in social work history.) We will come back to the question of gender and community again shortly.

(c)   There are a number of examples of the negative effects of close community ties. In their conclusion, Young and Willmott admit that belonging to a 'familiar society' has its disadvantages – 'If you know other people's business, they know yours' – and they acknowledge that feuds 'may be all the more bitter for being contained in such small space'. Again, this is something we will return to below.

The local community can be a source of friendship and support

Are we any closer now to defining a local community? Three important ideas seem to have emerged as characterising Bethnal Green in the 1950s. They are:

- *familiarity* – knowing and being known by other people whose lives are not dissimilar to your own

- *attachment* – a sense of belonging to the area, a loyalty to it and to those around you

- *mutual support* – a willingness to share information and resources in some ways and to help others.

Young and Willmott, as I have already said, were surprised to find so close-knit a community with such emphasis on family and neighbourly support in the heart of London. Did they overstate the positive side of it? Later commentators have criticised them for the rather rosy glow that the book leaves. They have suggested that we need to think much more critically about the economic circumstances of places like Bethnal Green, about the sexual division of labour, and about the way in which such communities could become inward-looking, defensive and antagonistic – especially towards minority groups. In Section 1.2, we will spend a little time on each of these issues in turn.

Key points

- The 1950s produced evidence of strong working-class communities based on long residence in an urban area and the presence of kin close by.

- Familiarity, attachment and mutual support can be said to be key aspects of such local communities.

1.2   Another look at Bethnal Green in the 1950s

The extract from Young and Willmott's study that you have read says nothing about the economic circumstances of those living in Bethnal Green in the 1950s. The chapter, after all, was designed to do something else. But the book as a whole is also rather reticent on the material circumstances of the families interviewed. Martin Bulmer, a more recent commentator, has reviewed what is known not just about Bethnal Green but about other communities too. He emphasises that in traditional working-class communities, what he describes as 'self-help networks' were:

> *a realistic response to low incomes, economic adversity and unpredictable domestic crisis. In the absence of state support for the relief in the home of illness, old age or unemployment, the 'safety net' for most families was the neighbourhood itself.*

> (Bulmer, 1986, pp. 49–50)

He then adds:

> *There were limits to the extent of mutual aid. It was useful to meet small-scale or very short-term material needs, and to deal with various forms of domestic crisis for a week or two. Neighbours could not provide*

adequate support for a household with too few wage earners – unmarried or deserted women with small children, widows and the elderly were more likely to have to move to the workhouse.

(Bulmer, 1986, p. 50)

Others, such as Philip Abrams, have argued that mutual aid networks of this kind came about as a response to very specific circumstances, rather than being merely the result of settled patterns of residence and family ties:

Internally, the networks of the traditional neighbourhood were indeed marked by collective attachment, reciprocity and trust. Externally, they were no less plainly marked by constraint, isolation and insecurity. Moreover, the internal characteristics were in large measure a product of the external characteristics, a way of life worked out to permit survival in the face of them.

(Abrams, in Bulmer, 1986, p. 92)

So the extent to which attachment and support featured in communities such as Bethnal Green should not be idealised or exaggerated. This will become a particularly important point when we consider in Section 2 how people have tended to see working-class communities like these as a model for 'community care' in the present.

What, then, can be said about gender issues? You saw how much of the community spirit displayed in Offprint 15 was among women. Young and Willmott include a full chapter on mothers and daughters, making very plain how close the relationship between them was, and how much reciprocal support it entailed. They asked the wives to describe their day and noted that 'Mum was rarely absent' in the replies that they received. Here is just one example:

After breakfast I bath the baby and sweep up. Then I go down the road shopping with Mum, Greta (one of the wife's married sisters who also has a child), and the three children. After dinner I clean up and then round about 2 o'clock I go out for a walk if it's fine with Mum and Greta and the children. I come back at about quarter to four to be in time for Janice when she gets back from school. She calls in at Mum's on her way home just to see if I'm there. This is an ordinary day. If anything goes wrong and I am in any trouble I always go running round to Mum's.

(Quoted in Young and Willmott, 1962, p. 47)

The chapter highlights the central place of the mother in her adult daughter's life and the important services she performs. Being there at childbirth and after the confinement is a major feature. If the wife gets contradictory advice from the welfare clinic and her Mum, the researchers observe, it is Mum who is usually listened to. Mum's availability to provide childcare is often crucial too in allowing the wife to go out to work. The mothers' traditional ideas about doing things were sometimes seen as old-fashioned by their daughters, but more often the daughter deferred to her mother, sometimes to the annoyance of her husband! The authors conclude that marriage divided the sexes into distinct roles and strengthened the mother–daughter tie. But they do not elaborate on this observation and they do not point out, as later commentators have, how much evidence they have in their study that the work of support and caring in the community is the work of women – work that has largely gone unacknowledged. In the 1980s, when feminists looked at government policies emphasising care by the community, they pointed out that this was in fact care by women – who, by this time, often did not have the support of their mothers close by. You saw in Unit 1 that the theme of isolation of young wives and mothers emerged from studies such as that by Hannah Gavron in the 1960s (Gavron, 1966).

Close-knit communities, I noted earlier, can give rise to hostility and conflict as well as mutuality and closeness. In a study carried out in the 1960s in the St Ann's district of Nottingham, a poor working-class area similar in many respects to Bethnal Green, Ken Coates and Richard Silburn emphasised the negative aspects of living on intimate terms with neighbours:

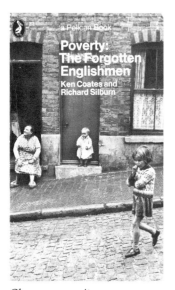

Close community – or cauldron of conflict?

> *such houses do not merely **separate** the people who live in them: they also bring people together, even when they may well not wish to be together. The backyards are not only a kind of semi-public forum and a playground: they are also, sometimes, a battleground. Contact between people is obviously more pronounced in a densely packed slum than would be normal on the straight avenues of the big estates.*
>
> *[...]*
>
> *Noise can very easily pass down the terrace from house to house. This means that if life is to be tolerable, it must conform to a common rhythm. If people's habits do not approximate to a very rigid common norm, their physical conditions will produce savage tensions ... People can learn tolerance in such surroundings, and become warmly involved in one another's problems. They can also learn jealous resentment, a cumulative and gnawing annoyance, a dumb but potent hostility.*
>
> (Coates and Silburn, 1970, pp. 105, 107)

Another negative aspect mentioned by Young and Willmott is the way attachment to family and community may be linked to reticence about inviting others into the home – and also to direct hostility to outsiders and newcomers. The examples given of suspicion of newcomers ('They're new here – they've only been here eighteen years') and hostility to people even from neighbouring boroughs ('they're a bit on the snobbish side') seem innocuous enough. However, it is not difficult to imagine such fierce local loyalties having more serious consequences. We may wonder how others who did not fit in with the norms of family and community would fare. We might want to find out how, for example, an unmarried mother, or a single gay man, might have been treated by the Bethnal Green community.

Young and Willmott do not mention such matters. But we do know, from other accounts, about the experience of members of minority ethnic groups in communities of this kind. There had been East End scenes of anti-Jewish riots in the 1930s. At the time that Young and Willmott were writing, it was quite common for landlords to display signs saying 'No Blacks or Irish'. And in other, similar, London boroughs in 1958, there were violent outbreaks of hostility towards black people:

> *Over a wide area, gangs of white teenagers armed with iron bars, sticks and knives, went, as they put it, 'nigger hunting'. In one evening's systematic and pitiless pursuit of isolated black victims, six West Indians were badly injured. By the end of August brawls, disturbances and racist attacks were a daily, and nightly, feature of life in north Kensington. Petrol bombs were thrown into black people's homes, including the homes of pregnant women. Such attacks were often*

preceded by a threatening letter or a shouted warning: 'We're going to raid you tonight if you don't clear out'. Attacks on black people spread to Kensal Green, north Paddington, and Harlesden, and were reported from as far afield as Southall, Hornsey, Islington, Hackney, and Stepney.

(Fryer, 1984, p. 379)

While it can be argued that violent attacks of this kind were the work of an extremist minority, it also takes some of the gloss off the picture of close, caring communities. We can see how the strong attachment to family and locality that produces a sense of belonging and solidarity may also result in hostility to and suspicion of anyone perceived to be 'different'.

Key points

- Although it is claimed that the sense of community in these areas depended on patterns of long residence and extended family ties, it can also be seen as the product of external circumstances, such as poverty and lack of resources.

- Much of the support and care in such communities was provided by women, especially through the close relationship between mothers and daughters.

- While displaying many attractive features, 'traditional' communities also had many negative aspects, such as internal conflicts and hostility to outsiders and newcomers.

1.3 Communities of place and communities of interest

So far we have been examining localised communities – those confined to a particular place. Does a community always have to be associated with a geographical area? Can we experience a sense of belonging to a community if it is not associated with a place? In practice people do use the term 'community' to refer both to geographical areas – including quite large areas where being familiar with others and feeling a sense of obligation to them is hardly feasible – and to communities that do not necessarily have a link with residence and territory in any clear way at all. Another way of looking at Bethnal Green, after all, would be to ask about the attachments people have, not only to the place but to groupings within it – communities based around churches, sports activities, local politics, and so on.

Let us think first about communities as large groupings – covering a whole country or perhaps a group of countries. Members of Parliament, for example, faced with lobbying by trade unions or employers, might say that they are there to make legislation 'in the interests of the whole community'. In this instance 'the community' means not some particular area but all those resident in England, Scotland, Wales and Northern Ireland (not all of whom, of course, will see themselves or wish to be considered as part of the same community). Similarly, there is the concept of the 'European community', a phrase people often use to describe the European Union. We know what this means – we could perhaps list the member states – but we would have to admit that not everyone feels a sense of membership and belonging in the Bethnal

Green sense. For many it is at least remote, and for some quite distasteful, to see themselves as part of political entities in this way. Use of the term 'community', then, can be a political act – a claim to unity and consensus that others might want to contest. Here, as in the local community sense, the word has a warm and positive air to it – one that might actually be unfounded.

What about communities that have little to do with place? As you have been working through the unit, you may have reflected that you did belong to something you would describe as a 'community' – except that it wasn't linked to a particular locality. You may have felt, for example, that a club or organisation that you belonged to, or a grouping of friends or workmates, exhibited many of the features of community that we have outlined. As Willmott has pointed out in his more recent work, the word 'community' is frequently used to describe 'people who share in common something other than physical proximity in the same place' (Willmott, 1989, p. 2). For this kind of group, Willmott uses the term 'interest community' or 'community of interest'.

Activity 3   **Many kinds of community**

Allow about 15 minutes   To tease out some of the ways in which we commonly use the term 'community' to mean a community of interest, write down, side by side, the two phrases below:

a .... community   the .... community

Then see how many different words you can insert into the spaces in each column. For example, you might think of the phrase 'a religious community', to go in the first column, or 'the gay community' to go in the second. Once you have a few phrases like this jotted down, consider what the differences are between the communities you have listed and a geographically localised community like Bethnal Green. Does the definition we used for a local community – people who are familiar with each other, who feel a sense of attachment and who offer mutual support – still hold?

Comment   Our course testers presented us with long lists in response to this. There were a lot of sports groups – the martial arts community and the ice hockey community, for example. Many felt that they shared a sense of community with others in their occupational group, even though people do not often refer to the social work community or the nursing community as such. Some gave examples of social movements and political pressure groups – the gay community fell into this kind of category. Then there were those whose belonging to the community was temporary – the student community was a favourite here. But we also had many examples of communities that people do not move in and out of. Among ethnic groups, for example, testers listed the black community, the Asian community and the Chinese community. This is interesting because it draws attention to the fact that there is a tendency to label a minority group a 'community', so distancing it from the majority community (no one referred to the white community, for example). People also gave names of specific religious organisations who had the term 'community' in their titles; we had reference to the Jewish community and the Muslim community and – from Northern Ireland – we had 'the two communities', sometimes meaning religion, sometimes meaning political affiliation.

Communities united by a common interest: demonstration against closure of local playcentres and Gay Pride march

There are many differences between the communities that appear in this list. Some are formally organised, some are not. Some are long-lasting, even lifelong, others are temporary. Some we choose, others we are regarded as belonging to whether we like it or not. The way in which 'community' can be used to refer to people other than oneself is something that we will pick up again in Unit 12 – where you will see that there is a danger of distancing yourself from the 'other' community and, in doing so, viewing its members as though they were all alike, rather than individuals.

Local communities can also be interest communities, or include communities of this kind within them. Such communities may emerge only when there is a particular threat or problem that brings people together. The one occasion on which I felt a 'sense of community' where I live was when there was a threat to re-open a disused railway line, as a busy freight line, within a few metres of the edge of our housing estate. The campaign against this development galvanised local people into *becoming* a community with a shared interest, if only temporarily: through the campaign, people got to know each other better, gained a greater sense of attachment to the local area, and supported each other in a common cause. There are many similar examples from other areas, such as when local people band together to campaign for an improvement to local provision, or to keep open a threatened local service.

Willmott has commented that, in communities of interest, what is shared is often more than 'interest', as that word is normally understood. It can also cover characteristics as varied as ethnic origin, religion, politics, occupation, leisure pursuit and sexual orientation. Willmott also mentions the rise of a new kind of interest community in recent years, one that has particular relevance for health and social care: 'This is the self-help or mutual aid group, composed of people who share a common condition or problem – examples are alcohol dependency, cancer, epilepsy, eczema and widowhood, and having stillborn children or children with a particular disability' (Willmott, 1989, pp. 2–3). We will be returning to Jim and Marianne from Unit 10 – members, we might say, of the drug users' community – later in this unit. We did not see their membership of this community helping them in any way in their search for better health. But later on, in Block 4, you will hear from someone with AIDS, who gives an account of how a strongly supportive network, offering advice, information and services, grew up in the gay community once the disease took hold.

Key points

- People may belong to communities based on interest or identity, rather than (or as well as) communities based on place.

- We may feel we belong to a number of communities of interest; this belonging is not fixed, but may change over a lifetime.

- Some people choose to identify with a particular community, others have that identity imposed on them.

- While some communities of interest are loosely organised or hardly organised at all, they may still offer important networks of care and support.

1.4 A loaded word again

Where does all this leave us, as far as understandings of community are concerned? You might recall how, in the very first unit of the course, we alerted you to the way that the word 'care' had been used at different times to mean different things, some of which were positive and some negative. Unit 1 argued that care was a 'loaded' word or, a little later, a 'contested' word. Care, in other words, is a concept that carries a lot of meanings, one that is used by ordinary people, by professionals and by academics. Because it is such a commonly used word, it is easy to skip past it, to think that the meaning is obvious to everyone. 'Community' is another such word. We need always to look at *who* is using it, in *what context* and to *signify what*. Some people have recommended that we should delete it from our vocabulary altogether, given its capacity to cause confusion. That is not practical. It is too well established. Just as Unit 1 suggested you use 'care' with care, so you need to use 'community' with care too.

Peter Willmott warns that the popularity of the word has not made its meaning any clearer. If anything, he argues, it is used even more ambiguously than in the past. And he adds:

> *Slippery though the notion of community may be, it is certain to continue in general usage, at least for the foreseeable future, whatever efforts are made to abolish it ... For the most part, we have to accept the word and make it as precise as possible.*

> *(Willmott, 1989, p. 5)*

In the next section, you will see how people do often evoke a dewy-eyed notion of community past, a mythical golden age of caring communities, which may not be at all helpful to understanding how care can be made available in the present.

There is a chapter in the Reader by Marjorie Mayo, entitled 'The shifting concept of community'. Ranging much more broadly over different historical periods and covering quite a number of the themes of this section, she too makes the point about how slippery the idea of community is and how it 'has been contested, fought over, and appropriated for different uses and interests to justify different politics, policies and practices'. I will ask you to read her chapter (Chapter 12) at the end of the unit, as a way of summarising and reviewing the themes as a whole. If you have time, however, you might want to take a first look at it now.

Section 2

Local communities past and present

It would be easy to form the impression that the localised community, in the sense in which we have examined it in Bethnal Green, has all but collapsed. Hardly a day goes by without the newspapers or television news carrying reports that seem to offer ample evidence of the absence, or at least a serious shortage, of the familiarity, attachment and mutual support that you earlier saw as being associated with a sense of community. Sensational stories about elderly neighbours left to die alone and unnoticed, children left 'home alone', estates torn apart by drug-taking and vandalism, children committing crimes at an ever-younger age: all of these are advanced as evidence of an apparent breakdown in any sense or spirit of community. You read about one such problem estate where drug-taking was a prevalent problem in Chapter 5 in the Reader, prepared by GP Tom Heller for Unit 10.

In response to concerns about community decline, some academic writers and political thinkers have called for a 'return' to community. As Dick Atkinson of the influential policy group Demos says:

> *The term community is on many lips today. Across Britain people are worrying as never before about the state of their streets and communities. There is a feeling that they have been weakened not only by market forces and technological change but also by the policies of successive governments. Many, including politicians of both left and right, are concerned about the lack of sufficiently robust local institutions close at hand for most citizens. Many also fear that the corollary of weak communities is that our belief in common values and our sense of responsibility for each other has atrophied ... most citizens see these issues in very practical ways, for example in relation to litter-free and safe streets, good schools and a sense of neighbourhood.*
>
> *(Atkinson, 1994, p. 1)*

This widespread perception of a breakdown in community life is often accompanied by a sense that, however we might define community, there was more of it about in the past. The very use of words like 'breakdown', 'decline' and 'weakened' implies that there was a time, usually unspecified, when local communities were stronger, closer and, above all, more caring.

2.1 Popular images of community

The two sides of this popular image – the breakdown in contemporary community life and nostalgia for an apparent golden age of community in the past – are brought together vividly in the following extract from Blake Morrison's book about the killing of two-year-old James Bulger by two ten-year-old boys in Merseyside in 1993. The Bulger killing, and particularly the fact that nobody who witnessed the events that led up to the murder did anything to prevent it happening, has itself become a powerful symbol of an apparent loss of community. In this passage, Morrison retraces the route through Bootle taken by the three boys, and paints a vivid picture of the local environment:

Fraternity is an important notion in the north, or used to be, in the days of industry and trade unions. An area like this would have considered itself a brotherhood, a community, poorer in wealth but stronger on family values than the spivvy, lounge-lizard south-east. These streets by the railway are called Groves, an urban pastoral: Elphin Grove, Rymer Grove, Golden Grove. Their names and shapes evoke Lowry paintings ... or early Coronation Street: *cramped but cosy, with father by the fire reading the racing finals, mother peacefully sewing, and the children with their penn'orth of mint humbugs playing hopscotch in the street. The smell of Woodbines, and fish and chips, and smoke rising from the chimney pots. That's how it was once, or fancied itself, a picture of mutual trust: the back door always open, people minding each other's business, friends who would give you their last shilling. Whereas now ... A ten-foot wiremesh fence sealing off the railway; backyards topped with broken glass; barbed wire coiled around each climbable post; burglar alarms and guard dogs; dogshit and cartons and dented drinks cans; dead quiet; no one in the streets. Not neighbourliness, but Neighbourhood Watch. Not brotherhood, but the* stumm, *useless, unpreventing cameras of Big Brother.*

(Morrison, 1997, p. 73)

Activity 4   **The past as a golden age of community**

Allow about 10 minutes   Look once again at the extract you have just read by Blake Morrison.

(a)   What kinds of image does Morrison evoke of community in the past?

(b)   What kinds of image does he evoke of the present?

(c)   What kind of account is this – does it tell the whole story about either past or present?

Comment   (a)   The picture of children playing in the street, presumably safe from the fear of traffic and violent crime, while their parents sit 'peacefully' indoors, conjures up a sense of peace and security, by contrast with the noise and anxiety of the present. The image of people leaving the back doors open and lending each other 'their last shilling' is a familiar, almost stereotypical picture of the 'ideal' community, based on relationships of mutual trust and care.

(b)   Morrison juxtaposes these warm images of the past with a bleak portrayal of present reality. The images – of barbed-wire fencing, closed-circuit cameras and empty streets – give a powerful sense of the fear or anticipation of crime. At the same time, the descriptions of litter and vandalism convey a sense of a lack of care and concern, as compared with the communal values of the past.

(c)   What Blake Morrison presents here is a personal 'snapshot' of what he saw. Although these are familiar images to us, we have no way of deciding whether his picture of the present is a representative one, or whether there are more positive aspects that he has failed to mention. The picture he conjures up of the past is almost a deliberate parody: he is fully aware that he is drawing on shared, popular images, rather than giving an accurate historical account.

Study skills: Styles of reporting

The previous study skills box discussed differences in the way information is gathered for news reports and for systematic research studies. But there are also differences in the language used for reporting. Blake Morrison does an excellent job of quickly sketching two contrasting images of community, but he uses language that would be out of place in a research report. Can you see how?

Go back through the paragraph and compare it with the writing in the Bethnal Green study. Underline any differences in style that you notice.

I picked out several things, including:

- *'An area like this would have considered itself'*. Morrison is talking of the 'area' as though it is a person – as though all the people in the area thought with a single mind. (He does it again later with 'fancied itself'.) We know what he means – and it works as a device for giving us a quick impression – but it seduces us into over-simplifying the situation. It also sets up a misleading 'model' of a community, as functioning like a single person with a single consciousness. Young and Willmott, by contrast, tell us what particular people *actually said*. They don't make sweeping generalisations about how people as a whole thought.

- *'... the spivvy, lounge-lizard south-east'*. This colourful descriptive language creates an instant impression of northern attitudes to the south-east. But the very strength of the imagery creates a problem. It plays on our emotions and encourages us to slip into accepting a widespread stereotype of northern attitudes. If we were satisfied with stereotypes then we could stick to mainstream media reporting. The point of research is to go beyond the stereotypes and encourage a questioning approach. For that reason – attractive though it is – vivid emotive language has to be excluded.

- *'... mother peacefully sewing'*. How do we know their lives were so peaceful? If we're free to sketch stereotyped pictures, we can all do it. How about 'mother cursing father for being down the pub, spending his wages'? The fact that an image is powerful does not mean it is realistic. Alternative images can easily be constructed. Yet images of 'ways of life' and 'types of people' have a persuasive force. They lull us into overlooking the complications of real life. So researchers need to be careful to avoid relying on imagery in their writing. They must try to describe what is – not tell us how to see it.

There are plenty of other things you could have underlined. But let's stop there and draw out some points for your own essay writing.

- Avoid 'personifying' society or institutions – 'society believes ...', 'care services hope to ...'.

- Avoid over-generalising – 'mothers simply want ...'.

- Avoid colourful descriptive language – 'the noble social worker valiantly essayed forth once more'.

- Don't rely on common stereotyped images as a form of shorthand – 'the rebellious teenager'.

 - Try to present a fair and objective account of what you describe (quickly look at Section 3.5 of Chapter 5, on page 152 of *The Good Study Guide*).

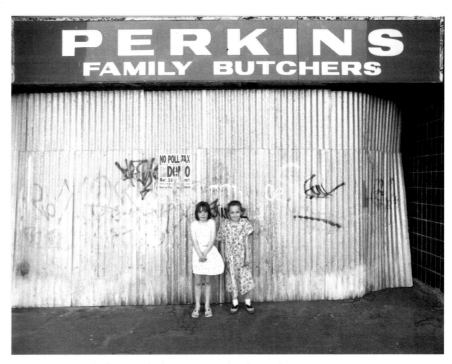

Community in decline? Aylesbury Estate, South London

The image of 'community past' that Morrison evokes is valuable to us here, precisely because it encapsulates images of community and of its breakdown that are so popular and so powerful. Such images are featured in countless nostalgic advertisements and historical dramas on television. Meanwhile, soap operas – *EastEnders* and *Coronation Street* being prime examples – present us with images of present-day communities which seem to be based on nostalgia for 'community past' – communities in which everyone knows everyone else, people's lives overlap, and neighbours are always on hand to talk over problems and lend advice and support. The popularity of programmes like these tells us something, perhaps, about a widespread hankering after some ideal of 'close' community – a community in which people met their neighbours regularly at the pub or the corner shop, knew everything about each other's lives, and acted as an informal support network to each other in times of need. Jeremy Seabrook, describing life on a housing estate in Walsall in the 1980s, points out that it is ironic, but perhaps significant, that such programmes should be so popular when real communities are perceived to be in decline:

> *It is impossible to escape the irony that on this estate at half past seven on Monday and Wednesday evenings a very considerable number of the people are watching* Coronation Street *on TV: that frozen eternal working-class street where fictitious lives have come to take on such significance for us. Do they offer us a sense of continuity when there seems to be so little in real life? Does the shadow of community give us reassurance of a substance that has departed? There is something more than soap opera for the millions of people who watch it each week: it has the fascination of something that endures, when the actual communities it claims to represent are in the throes of dissolution and change.*

(Seabrook, 1984, p. 34)

But if ideas about past communities are so much part of popular thinking and so imbued with nostalgia, they may well misguide us about the present. They may cause us to overlook pockets of traditional community that remain and fail to see the diversity of ways of living in the present. We may fail, for instance, to see new forms of community – new kinds of network and social bond, based perhaps on communities of interest rather than communities of place – that have become available in the present. What, then, is actually known about the nature and extent of community today? Do communities like Bethnal Green survive? Can they be, have they been and should they be recreated in some way?

2.2 The changing context of community

As you read the extract from Young and Willmott earlier, it may be that you recognised some of the features of 'traditional' communities as familiar from your own experience. Examples of local communities bound together by extended family ties and long-standing residence do still exist in modern Britain. Bethnal Green itself, although it has changed dramatically in many ways since the 1950s, still displays some of the features of a close community identified by Young and Willmott. The accompanying box is a brief description, supplied by a present-day resident, of the make-up of the modern Bethnal Green 'community'.

The Bethnal Green Community today

Walking round Bethnal Green today it is still possible to recognise elements of the Bethnal Green described by Young and Willmott in the mid-1950s. The areas are still clearly differentiated, although the boundaries are less clear. Brick Lane and the Boundary Street Estate are still populated by those some locals would see as 'newcomers': today it is predominantly Asian, and Brick Lane is famous for its wide variety of Indian restaurants. It is also a major centre for the wholesale clothing industry, ranging from cheap chainstore clothing to leatherwear, but still apparently run as small businesses. The Bethnal Green Road area is still predominantly populated by skilled and unskilled manual workers with little evidence of white-collar workers or professionals – remnants of the furniture business remain, with a few of the original workshops still in use although many are now empty. The Jewish community has gone elsewhere, but many of the original inhabitants remain and much of the property is still privately rented. Taxi drivers, shopkeepers and cafe owners are evident. There are also artists' studios and a growing artists' community, although in Bethnal Green this is more a spillover from the surrounding areas of Spitalfields, Hackney and Whitechapel. There is still a strong sense of community in this area, with evidence of the close and regular contact between the generations if not the wider family of the 1950s. One recent incomer says:

> We bought our house from a couple who had lived there for 30 years and came from Spitalfields. He had been an electrician. They moved three miles away to live next door to a married daughter. The couple opposite took over the rental of their house from the wife's mother when she died – the wife was born in the house and brought up her own family there. They are frequent visitors and clearly live nearby. There is still a very strong sense of community in the street with a lot of friendly interest and close observation of every movement – we were told there have been no burglaries there for 30 years.

Although there is clearly tension between the different ethnic groups there is an overriding sense of being a community still. Apart from Brick Lane, the ethnic groups are not divided into clear areas, and shops and cafes are owned by predominantly white and Asian families but also by black, Italian, Vietnamese, Iranian, Chinese and Greek families. Bow still has many small neat houses with neat gardens, but many are privately owned rather than rented and the doorsteps are not whitened now. The white-collar and professional classes have moved in to some extent although it is very patchy – a few streets, especially near Victoria Park, look as if they have gone 'upmarket', but most do not. There is a sprinkling of vegetarian restaurants and art galleries along the first few hundred yards of the Roman Road, but it is not sustained. There is still a recognisable sense of familiarity, attachment and mutual support at least in parts of Bethnal Green today.

A key aim of this section is to tease out the factors that have given rise to change and to come to a less extreme view than that presented by Morrison or by some of the newspaper accounts that you might read (the page overleaf gives an example).

Activity 5   **Change in a lifetime**

Allow about 10 minutes   Set out below is an account given by a working-class woman in Belfast to researchers recording working people's views of changes in their lifetimes. The book was written to be used by working-class people themselves in community education projects. Read the account through, then:

(a)   list the factors this woman identifies as changing the community from that she knew as a child

(b)   see if you can add any other sources of change to her list.

My memories of my childhood, coming home from school, was the big fire in the hearth. The fireplaces then you had to black-lead them and you had to use the emery paper on the stainless steel that was around them ...

When you think of the street you lived in, the neighbours were neighbours, if you get the meaning? If there was hardship, the hardship was shared, so were the good times. If you had something that you could give to the neighbours to make it a little bit easier for them, then that's what you did. That was the companionship and the neighbourliness that existed then, but doesn't exist now. Now you have the large estates going up, and you have first and foremost the width of the streets which divides neighbours from the far side of the street, the opposite side. Things are so materialistic now that everyone has to own a car, they have to own a colour television, and they have to have the telephone. It's: 'I have to have', it's not a case of needing a thing. It's just to have it in order to be better than the other person.

(Quoted in McNamee and Lovatt, 1987, pp. 19–20)

Comment   (a)   Change in street and housing design is the first factor this woman singles out as transforming the communities of her childhood. More acquisitive attitudes are another factor in her mind, associated,

'If you see anything you keep your mouth shut'

by NIGEL ROSSER

THEY named the pub on the corner Disgraceland, and as you enter the vast council estate there is a sense of shame that urban deprivation in the capital can reach these levels.

Less than a mile from Prime Minister Tony Blair's pleasant Islington terrace, the Marquess Estate is a running urban sore even the council wants pulled down. It is a place where children as young as seven run with gangs of youths that call themselves "The Marquess Boys" or the "Packerton Mob" and roam the maze of Seventies walkways and crumbling low-rise housing blocks fighting, swearing, kicking anything in their way.

It is here that two women made the mistake of telling police what they saw when 19-year-old Scott McMullin was killed in a gang fight in April last year.

The locals said it was all because someone had thrown a pot of yoghurt over his little brother. The locals also said the two women, who are fighting for re-housing in the High Court as a result, were mad to come forward and give evidence.

The police on the Marquess Estate are viewed by these boys — and, sadly, many of their parents — as the enemy. Anyone who talks to them risks a brick through their window. Or worse.

Around 10 criminal families, passing violence down from generation to generation, set the anti-social tone of the neighbourhood, which, lawless and unloved, has become a breeding ground for delinquency and hatred. Just ask residents. One woman, walking the bull terrier she keeps for protection, said: "The boys up there think they own the estate. It's like a teenage Mafia up there.

"If you see anything you keep your mouth shut, keep yourself to yourself. I won't let my boy out. He's seven and when he does mix with them he comes back giving me pure cheek, he changes something awful. I'd kill myself if I thought I had to live here for much longer."

Asked for her name, the woman summed up the Marquess Road code of silence: "I don't mind talking to you, but I've got my little boy to think of."

Another woman, who crams five children into her three room flat said: "They want to blow up the place. Last year, my eight-year-old son had a brick thrown at him as he walked under an arch and it split his head open. We knew the family who did it.

The police went round and didn't press charges because the boy who did it was under-age.

"We didn't hear any more about it for about three weeks then my son was cycling past and the mother told her boy to push him off his bike and start kicking him."

Women driven from homes for helping police convict killers

The Marquess Estate (above) and (left) the Standard's story about the two residents who helped detectives

Bruno Cattini believes the community has died but grants could improve the estate

She added: "People who talk to the police get victimised: their windows get smashed, or they'll take it out on your kids — and I've got five kids.

"My eldest son is 16, but I can't let him out on his own on this estate. I can't trust him not to get involved."

Another resident said: "Even for petty things you'll get a kid knee high to a grasshopper telling you: 'If you say anything, you're dead'." A policeman added: "I don't think people hate us, I think they're scared to like us."

John Hinchy, the father of Liam Hinchy, who was convicted of actual bodily harm for his part in Mr McMullin's death, said: "There are always problems with gangs around here. Most of these boys grew up together. It is a terrible place to be if you have teenage boys."

But, as children scrawl pro-IRA graffiti, hurl dog faeces at homes and drink cans of strong, cheap lager into the early hours there is hope from the £9.5 million grant and a further £40 million from the council and housing associations that could transform the estate in eight years.

As Bruno Cattini, 72, said: "The community has died, but I think this will help. Frankly I thought there was more trouble when I came here 20 years ago, anyway. That's when it all started."

although she does not say it in so many words, with higher incomes. The phone, the TV and the car to her are signs of materialist thinking. We might want to add that they also mean changes in how people spend time and how they relate to each other.

(b)   You might have mentioned a wide range of other possible changes. I don't expect you to have listed all the developments covered below, or in anything like this degree of detail. The discussion that follows draws on work by some of those who have studied the ways in which community has changed in recent years.

Changing patterns of residence

Young and Willmott claimed that one of the key factors contributing to a sense of community in Bethnal Green was that many people had lived in the area for a long time, some for all their lives. There are some areas of the country where this is still true, but they are increasingly an exception. Changing patterns of work, in particular, mean that fewer people remain in the area where they grew up, or remain in the same area for the whole of their working lives. Many traditional working-class communities were based on large, single industries, such as shipbuilding, mining or steel production. As these industries have declined and other kinds of employment have taken their place, so people's ties to a particular location have weakened. Many people now find themselves working for organisations that are smaller-scale, or dispersed over a wider area. It is increasingly unusual for local communities to be made up of people who mostly do the same kind of work, so this important focus for community life – with its sense of shared routines, and common concerns and rituals – has tended to disappear. On the other hand, many people in working-class areas can find themselves thrown out of work, but without the resources to move away from the area to find alternative employment.

Improved transport and communications

Many people's mobility has increased in other ways too. Young and Willmott give the example of a woman who had been out of Bethnal Green only once in her life, for a day trip to Southend. In the past, travel beyond the immediate locality was difficult and expensive, and some people rarely left the town or village where they lived. Today, cheaper and faster transport means that people are able to travel further from where they live, to work, to shop or for leisure pursuits. The result of this is that:

> *The local neighbourhood is no longer the centre for many of the activities of the more advantaged, including a considerable proportion of the working class. To take but one mundane example, shopping is typically no longer carried out at the local corner shop, but at the supermarket, in the town-centre or at the out-of-town shopping mall, for the three-fifths of the population who have a car, plus some of those who do not.*
>
> (Bulmer, 1987, p. 32)

In addition, technology has opened up people's lives beyond the local community in other ways, with telephones, television and radio, and now computers, bringing them into contact with a wide range of people and experiences, way beyond the confines of their geographical community. All of this reduces people's attachment to, and dependence on, the place where they live and the people who live close by.

Changes in transport and lifestyle have contributed to the break-up of traditional communities

Increased social mobility

Geographical mobility is one thing, but the population is also generally more *socially mobile* than in previous generations – there are more chances to gain an education or training and for people to improve their jobs and standard of living. The older residents of Bethnal Green, who had lived in the area all their lives, had experienced very little change in their circumstances. For the generations that have followed them, however, things have been very different. Although a considerable proportion of people are still caught in the poverty trap and in poor housing, others have seen their lot improve in the past 40 years, as a result of universal free education, the establishment of a comprehensive welfare system and generally increasing prosperity. Even if class distinctions and other inequalities have not vanished, people now have an expectation that they *should* be able to change their social status and improve their prospects. Once again, this means people moving around to find a better job (or any job at all), or a bigger house, and thus feeling less tied to one particular location or group of people.

Privatisation of life

Another change in people's everyday experience has been what some writers have described as the increasing 'privatisation' of life. Here is Jeremy Seabrook again describing a poor working-class neighbourhood in Walsall:

> *In one sense, people don't live in the neighbourhood at all. There they simply exist. The living is done inside – not only inside the houses, which, in spite of the shabbiness and the poverty, are for the most part warm and not without comfort, but inside the head, where the fantasies and the images from the media and the television penetrate poorest and well-to-do alike, with their invitation to escape, to dream, and to forget.*

> *(Seabrook, 1984, p. 13)*

Over the past 100 years, technology has transformed the way in which most people spend their leisure time, with radio and television, and more recently video films and computers, creating a world of entertainment which both encourages people to spend more time in the home, and at the same time connects them to a world of experiences and possibilities far beyond the boundaries of the local community. Bulmer sees this as a longer-term trend, beginning with improvements to housing and changing patterns of family life in the Victorian period. He also observes:

> *It is only in the second half of the twentieth century that 'privatisation' has come to have particular connotations of withdrawal from the public sphere and attenuation of community ties.*
>
> (Bulmer, 1987, pp. 59–60)

The changing experience of women

The community Young and Willmott depicted was one in which women were highly visible – meeting at the local shops, standing talking in the street (as shown on the cover of the Penguin edition of the book). It was also one in which mothers and daughters were able to be in constant contact with one another. The changes I have just considered have had a dramatic impact on this. Where old housing has been cleared, new homes with gardens and on wider streets make casual contact less frequent. New consumer goods, the 'labour-saving devices' that often meant more frequent washing and cleaning, and ever-rising standards of household consumption, have kept women busy indoors and, for many, the weekly visit to the supermarket has taken them away from the daily conversations at the local shops. Of course, these changes have not affected everyone equally, and many people, particularly in some inner-city areas and poorer estates, still live in close contact with neighbours and depend on local shops and facilities.

Most important of all, though, have been changing trends in women's paid employment. Married working-class women have always worked – earlier in the twentieth century, they could be found not only working in factories but also taking in washing, having lodgers or doing outwork at home for the local factory. By the 1950s, with labour shortages, manufacturing plants were setting up the 'twilight shift', enabling a woman to work in the evening, once her husband had come home and was able to mind the children. Many of the women interviewed by Young and Willmott, all with children under 15, were in paid work. Census figures show that, overall, around one-quarter of all married women were in paid employment in 1951, a figure that had

The growth in women's employment since the 1950s has helped to change people's experience of community

risen to almost half by 1971, and that continued to rise thereafter (Lewis, 1992). In more recent decades, when unemployment has been high, there has been a growth in the part-time jobs that are taken up by women who juggle these jobs with childcare, which still often involves reliance on family. Among the fewer people on the streets of Bethnal Green during the day, then, we can expect to see more unemployed men, and more women hurrying to and from part-time work. Generally speaking, working-class mothers and daughters are not available to offer the kind of reciprocal support that cemented community in the past. Middle-class women too have experienced change. Although there is still much evidence of inequalities in pay and status between the sexes, greater educational opportunity, legislation outlawing sex discrimination in employment, and women's own rising expectations about their right to paid work and careers, have all opened up horizons and meant that, in general, women are not to be seen in the local community in the way they were in the past.

What is the upshot of all these changes? The overriding impression is that, for many people in Britain today, the locality in which they live is much less important than it was for previous generations. People are much less dependent than they were on the local community to meet their needs. It is important to remember, once again, that the changes I have been outlining affect different sections of the population in different ways. In particular, it has to be remembered that those with resources are the main beneficiaries of such radical changes. Here is Bulmer again, in a particularly important passage, talking about 'the advantaged' – in others words, the better-off:

> *The advantaged command economic strength and educational skills which permit them to negotiate their way across the world, establishing work, leisure and friendship ties across a relatively wide geographical area, going well beyond the neighbourhood, and participating in a number of different social networks ... The disadvantaged – particularly the unemployed, chronically sick, single parents, the elderly on low incomes and the mentally and physically handicapped – lack such skills and the choice which that confers.*
>
> *(Bulmer, 1987, p. 32)*

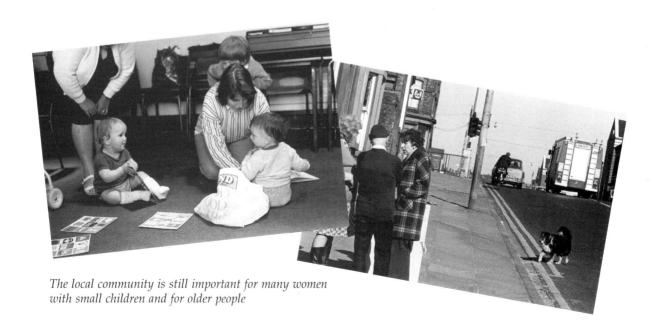

*The local community is still important for many women
with small children and for older people*

While a majority of people depend less on the local community than in previous generations, Bulmer reminds us that the locality remains the centre of their social world not only for the poor but for most young children, for non-working mothers and for many older people, particularly those among the over-75s who are unsteady or infirm. For these groups the immediate community of place is still very important. Not everyone is able to travel beyond it for work or pleasure, or to plug into the latest technology within their homes. Think, for example, of Arthur Durrant in the case study in Block 1, who was very much tied to the home. Those who are disabled or housebound, as well as people who are out of work or poor, are likely to feel more tied to, and therefore more dependent on, the local community, than others. In fact, their needs may actually have *increased*, both because of new economic conditions such as long-term unemployment and cuts in state welfare provision, but also because of the very weakening of local community networks that we have been describing.

Key points

- Social and economic changes have weakened many people's ties to and dependence on the local community.

- Some groups, particularly those who are poor or disadvantaged in other ways, still rely on the local community to meet many of their needs.

2.3 Recreating tradition – a model for today

Can the 'traditional' form of community that we have examined in Bethnal Green serve as a model for communities today? Some people are so convinced it can that they are taking deliberate steps to create it. They are using a form of what is often called 'social engineering' – trying to design and build ways of life much as we design and build machines. The reading in Activity 6 describes a recent proposal to create a 'sense of community' located in Manningham in Bradford.

Activity 6   **Planning to create a community**

Allow about 20 minutes

Turn to the Offprints Book and read Offprint 16 'Love thy neighbour' by Christine Jeavans. She describes a plan to encourage 'the rebirth of the community life' in a modern setting. You will see that a key element in the plan is a proposal to make residence in the area conditional on signing 'a formal pledge to be neighbourly'. You may well find you have strong reactions for or against this proposal. Jot them down and we will come back to them in the next activity. For now, note down your answers to the following two questions:

(a) The proposers of the scheme clearly believe it offers benefits. What do they claim these are?

(b) The Manningham scheme rests on an assumption that the 'neighbourly spirit' has all but vanished. What reasons are suggested for this decline in the sense of community?

Comment   (a)   One of the main suggested benefits is in terms of employment –
                particularly, providing assistance with childcare to enable women to
                enter the labour market and to widen their choice of work. It is
                also claimed that the scheme will help to reduce violence and crime
                on the estate, by encouraging 'feelings of unity and community
                pride'. You can probably think of other likely benefits that are not
                mentioned in the article. If the scheme is successful in encouraging
                people to carry out errands, repairs and so forth for their neighbours,
                then many local people will feel the benefits, but in particular the
                more vulnerable and needy members of the community and
                those whose work and home responsibilities leave them very short
                of time.

          (b)   Anil Singh, Director of the Manningham Housing Association, which is
                promoting this initiative, pinpoints 'lack of investment' in public sector
                housing. This, he claims, has led to 'a high turnover of tenants who
                have little or no reason to care about each other'.

You will have noticed that Michael Young and the Bethnal Green study
figure as important to the thinking behind this contemporary
development. Jeavans attributes Young's criticisms of housing policy in
part to his experience with the Bethnal Green study. Young and
Willmott found that the close family ties they discovered in Bethnal
Green were severely curtailed when people moved out to new council
houses in Essex (a part of the argument that was not included in
Offprint 15 which you read for Activity 2). Jeavans implies that these
findings influenced Young's own attitudes to current housing policy.

Young himself has explained more recently:

> *Working-class housing used to be for rent, and the rent collector who*
> *chose the new tenants when there was a vacancy ordinarily followed the*
> *nomination by mothers of their daughters and sons. The 'speaking for'*
> *system operated across the country.*

(*Young and Lemos, 1997, p. 2*)

Compared with the rent collector, local authorities took decisions in a
quite different way. When they demolished the old cottages as slums
and built new dwellings, they allocated their new houses not according
to 'social need' in the sense Young explains – the old practice – but
strictly according to set rules of 'housing need' – people had to get the
right number of 'points' to be rehoused. The result was that many
relatives and neighbours were scattered.

> *Housing need cannot be thrown aside. But the social need for building*
> *and sustaining communities should come to the fore. Where people have*
> *to move, sons and daughters and grandparents should be brought together*
> *– in the interests of mutual aid – wherever they want to be, along with*
> *relatives in the vitally important Third Age: people neither old nor young*
> *who can help with the care needed by both.*

(*Young and Lemos, 1997, p. 3*)

The Manningham proposal, and the kinds of view put forward here by
Young, are not without their critics, as Offprint 16 makes clear.

Activity 7   **Where do you stand?**

Allow about 15 minutes

Would you sign a pledge promising to be a good neighbour, as a condition of moving into a new area? What problems, if any, can you foresee with such a scheme? Spend some time reflecting on these questions. You may want to compare your response to the proposal with those of family members or friends. Look too at what some of the critics have said, as summarised in the final paragraphs of Offprint 16. Do you agree with these criticisms or are you broadly sympathetic to the scheme proposed by the Manningham Housing Association?

Comment

My own response is that the proposal seems fine in theory. I can see the personal benefits of being part of such a scheme – getting help with childcare, or with burdensome tasks like gardening or household repairs, for example. I would also quite like to live in an area where there was a strong sense of neighbourliness and mutual support, if this could be achieved without the conflicts that, as we have seen, tend to be a feature of close-knit communities. The lazy part of me would probably resent being required to 'do my bit' as a good neighbour, but I would probably feel it was the right thing to do!

On the other hand, I can see some problems with a scheme of this kind. I tend to think of my relationships with my neighbours as a matter of choice and individual preference, rather than as something imposed from outside. I would like to know my neighbours better, but I would prefer to think of neighbourliness as arising out of shared interests, rather than as the result of a planned scheme. Finally, who would be the judge of whether I had been 'neighbourly' enough, and on what basis? And what happens if I feel that one of my neighbours hasn't kept to their side of the bargain?

All this is to look at the matter from a very personal point of view. Jeavans quotes Cora Carter, of the National Tenants and Residents Federation, arguing that the Manningham proposal misses the point. The underlying problem, in her view, is not to do with people themselves and their lack of community spirit. Instead, it is to do with lack of employment creation and lack of investment. This leaves some people disadvantaged, and some young people, without hope or prospects, can sometimes turn to crime. What she wants to see is what is known as a *structural* solution, not an *individual* one. Rather than trying to change the people, she would say, we need to change their circumstances. Notice, for example, how she says that social breakdown and rising crime 'is a symptom and not a cause'. Cora Carter does not think you can impose neighbourliness, but she has another point too. Should we set more rules for tenants than for homeowners? Where is the justice in that? (For more information on changes in social housing, see the accompanying box.)

Structural change in social housing

Local authorities in Britain, and the Housing Executive in Northern Ireland, have long administered public sector housing – referred to here as social housing – as a public policy response to poverty and housing need. Recent research by Roger Burrows shows some unexpected trends. Far from the sector simply shrinking as a result of purchase of council houses, which was speeded up and encouraged during the Thatcher governments of the 1980s, he demonstrates a great deal of movement into and out of social housing and dramatic changes in the social composition of estates. Malcolm Dean, summarising the results for *Search*, the influential magazine of the Joseph Rowntree Foundation, explains:

> *two quite distinct communities are emerging within the sector with quite profound differences in culture and lifestyle. At one end are the established elderly residents, who have lived in social housing all their lives and who remember a time when having a council house was a desirable goal. At the other end are the new, younger residents, frequently suffering from multiple problems; unemployment, poverty, poor work skills and perhaps mental illness and drug abuse as well.*

> (Dean, 1997, p. 11)

Trends such as these, the research suggests, are increasingly undermining the balance of the community, narrowing its social base to the homeless, the poor and the unemployed. Dean's picture is one of 'Americanisation' of social housing, with deteriorating standards and low horizons. He calls for major changes in housing policy to remedy this.

Perhaps, then, we should not try forcibly to recreate an idealised past, but accept that social and economic changes have altered many people's lives, and that there is no going back to former models of community. We need to understand the different lives that people lead and find ways of responding through social and economic policies to improve environments and increase the likelihood that people can obtain worthwhile jobs. At the same time, there is a need to work through the health and social care services to support those who remain vulnerable.

Key points

- Some initiatives have attempted deliberately to recreate 'traditional' communities. They have sometimes been accompanied by calls for a radical change in public housing policy.

- There are doubts as to whether such proposals are workable or desirable in a society that emphasises choice, diversity and difference.

- There is also a view that we should not look to a past where close-knit communities arose out of economic hardship, but instead rethink the notion of care and support to match the more varied circumstances of today.

Section 3
Can today's communities care?

As far as this course is concerned, the point of giving so much
attention to ideas of community is to discover how feasible it is to rely
on the local community – people living close by – to provide care for
those who need it, with support from health and social care services.
Bethnal Green wives in the 1950s, as you have seen, turned to their
mothers for advice on and practical assistance with the care of
children. And those mothers were themselves cared for when they
were old and infirm by their daughters and their daughters' children.
But you have seen in the previous section that many of the factors that
sustained this supportive community of women have been changed.
Today, both the wife and her mother are likely to be in employment,
and arranging childcare while women do paid work is often a major
undertaking. There are questions too as to whether neighbours are
available or prepared to help out.

Questions such as these have very immediate and practical
consequences in the climate of today's policies on community care.
The 1990 NHS and Community Care Act (as you saw both in Unit 3
and in Unit 10) is designed to allow people who need care to live as
independently as possible and to have a say in the services they
receive. But it also makes assumptions that people needing community
care have resources and support on which those services can build.
The Act, for example, refers to networks of informal carers and
states that:

> *the first task of publicly provided services is to support and where
> possible strengthen these networks of carers.*

> *(para. 3.2)*

It then goes on to explain that a key aim is:

> *to identify where these caring networks have broken down or
> cannot meet the needs and decide what public services are desirable to
> fill the gap.*

> *(para. 3.3)*

Jim and Marianne in Unit 10 were not part of a community where kin
and neighbours might provide help, and you saw what happened to
them. But some of the other service users you have met in the course
have had different experiences. We need to get some sense of the variety
of patterns of living and patterns of support from community and kin.
We need to shift the focus away from communities of place and
communities of interest, towards more specific *networks* of family,
friends and neighbours.

3.1 Evidence of variety in networks of support and care

To start thinking about networks, I approached a number of people and asked them what they did when they had an attack of flu – a bad one, one that meant there was nothing for it but to take to your bed for two or three days. I collected a range of answers. One person had a mother who lived nearby. On a really bad day, she did the necessary shopping, made tea for the school-age children and put them to bed. Several said they would pop in to the neighbour, who would run an errand or two. One had a sister some miles away and said that, despite the distance, 'we always look out for each other'. A third person I asked was silent for a moment and then said:

> *I guess I have it organised like a military campaign – I live on my own, there is no one I can ask. I always have heat-treated milk in the cupboard and bread in the freezer. You can feel these things coming on – so I nip out and get the cold cure treatment, then I line up my survival kit by the bed.*

Rather than ask you to try this exercise for yourself, I want you to think about support networks – or lack of them – a little more in the next activity through looking back at some of the people you have already met in the course. We will return to Jim and Marianne for the next activity, comparing them with Mr and Mrs Bright from Block 2, Unit 7. You heard a lot about the Brights on Audio Cassette 2, side 1, but it will probably be enough just to read about them in the relevant sections of Unit 7 to refresh your memory.

Activity 8

Allow about 30 minutes

Who has networks in place to help provide care?

After a brief look at the relevant parts of Unit 7 and Unit 10, compare the resources that the Brights have at their disposal with those available to Marianne and Jim. To help you, here are some headings:

- informal networks and neighbourhood ties
- family
- availability of informal care
- knowledge of statutory systems
- existing contact with voluntary agencies
- personal and material resources.

Comment

Resources	Mr and Mrs Bright	Marianne and Jim
Informal networks and neighbourhood ties	Strong, long-term neighbourhood network, good relations with neighbours. People know Mr Bright and can be relied on to guide him home when he wanders off with the dog.	Some ties with other homeless people and drug users around the city centre. Gives them social contact, street knowledge, but also may encourage them to carry on using heroin.
Family	Members distant, but concerned and involved enough to prompt Mrs Bright to consider applying for help.	Marianne's parents distant, and disillusioned with previous failures, such as the rented flat.
Availability of informal care	Mrs Bright is the informal carer.	Can Jim be seen as a potential informal carer?
Knowledge of statutory systems	When we met them, Mrs Bright had been using services for some time. She knew her care manager, and where to turn when she had problems. Her GP was her first port of call.	Beginning users of community care services, but great familiarity with benefits system, as well as primary care services. Strongest personal contact is with GP.
Existing contact with voluntary agencies	Mrs Bright is a member of her local Carers' Group.	Weak links with drug agencies, perhaps some contact with local soup kitchens for homeless people.
Personal and material resources	Own home, fully furnished, car.	A couple of sleeping bags, possessions in a few plastic bags.

Comparing the two couples in this way is a reminder that 'community' and the networks it offers can mean very different things to different people. For the Brights, 'community' apparently has the traditional meaning of the neighbourhood and people in it who are known to and potentially helpful to them. For Jim and Marianne, 'community' is not something local at all. Insofar as they might feel part of a community, it is a community of interest – people similar to them scattered around a large geographical area and not necessarily in contact with and directly helpful to each other in times of need. It would be very important for a care manager, faced with these contrasting situations, to be aware of the different resources each couple can bring to the situation and to design a care package accordingly.

Another example we can draw on is Baldock and Ungerson's study of stroke sufferers in Kent. You read an extract from this study as Chapter 29 in the Reader for Unit 10. In the longer report from which your reading was drawn (Baldock and Ungerson, 1994), people mentioned help that they received from neighbours. They did this frequently enough for the researchers to list 'neighbours' as a significant category in the mixed economy of care. Their more detailed findings show that help from neighbours included:

- transport for relatives, to and from hospital, before the stroke victim was discharged

- provision of meals or housework for the partner left at home

- shopping, delivery of prescriptions

- help with gardening and household repairs

- lifts to day care, outpatient appointments, etc.

- 'keeping an eye out' for people.

They also noted that some local organisations, like churches or Round Table members, also offered various kinds of help, free or at nominal charges. Not all of what neighbours did came for free. Some neighbours accepted gifts of reciprocal services, others were willing to take small payments.

Activity 9   Creating a network of support

Allow about 15 minutes

Glance again at Chapter 29 by Baldock and Ungerson, in the Reader. Look at each of the four types of behaviour they describe – consumerism, privatism, welfarism and clientalism. What can you learn about habits of relying on others when you need care?

Comment   Consumerists, it seems, would perhaps rely on family, but they bought services in the way that they bought goods. Interestingly, this was not just the prerogative of the well-off. Baldock and Ungerson refer to a couple whose network could be said to include the local taxi driver, builder, grocer and butcher, even though small payments were given.

People who took a privatist stance had real trouble when they needed care. Our 'military campaigner' is like the woman they describe who found she had to create a network and who experienced asking for help as 'excruciating'. (I referred to the 'privatisation of life' as an important trend in Section 2.2.)

It is less clear whether welfarists and clientalists had networks they could use. The welfarist clearly looked to NHS and social services as the first port of call – expecting a range of services as a right. The clientalist more passively accepted what services were on offer, however rigid and inconvenient they were.

So it is not just a matter of where you live, how mobile you have been and what financial resources you have – there are, as Baldock and Ungerson put it, 'fundamental values according to which people live their lives'. We cannot make neat generalisations about the networks of support available to working-class and middle-class people or about what those who are well-off and those with lower incomes will do. People in the Kent study had not signed a contract as in the Manningham proposal, but it was possible, if they felt they wished to do it, to negotiate and sometimes to pay for help.

3.2 Trends and counter-trends

Small-scale and local studies are important in building a picture of the quality of life and the gaps in services in particular settings. The case of the Brights and the study by Baldock and Ungerson are important correctives to the gloomy view that community has died completely, and that, because of modern trends (greater mobility, privatisation of life, and so on), people are cut off from family and neighbourhood support systems when it comes to care. But can everyone rely on such support?

The Rowntree Research Unit carried out an extensive investigation into 'patterns of neighbourhood care' in a wide variety of locations throughout the UK (Snaith, 1989). The research consisted primarily of 'street studies' whose aim was to identify the extent of informal care by members of local communities. The main finding of the study was a negative one. As the authors put it: 'Essentially the study was a search for "community care" and found a dearth of it' (Snaith, 1989, p. 2). However, the research team were keen to emphasise that this does not mean that people no longer care at all for their neighbours:

> This does not mean that helping and support was not happening ... but rather that, in general, help and support was not being provided on anything like an intensive basis for reasons of people living near one another. Simply living near someone ... could facilitate the giving of help, but did not itself determine that help would be given.

> (Snaith, 1989, p. 2)

The authors of the study maintain that most neighbourhood care in 'traditional' communities was undertaken by kin. And they add that this is even more the case today owing to 'the disappearance or attenuation of the social context which produced mutual aid among non-related local people in working-class neighbourhoods'. On the other hand, where 'informal neighbourhood care' by non-relatives does occur today, the researchers found that it is activated by people sharing a 'social context' beyond merely being neighbours. In the case of people who were not related, the study found two particular groups of people among whom the provision of local care was evident – older people and non-employed women with children. The researchers state that 'both groups represented a kind of survival of the traditional patterns of neighbouring'. The relationships underpinning care of this nature were ones of 'exchange and reciprocity which had in effect often extended to friendship'.

Bulmer argues that support structures at neighbourhood level do not emerge spontaneously in modern societies, but have to be deliberately nurtured. The Rowntree research was able to focus on initiatives that set out to create such structures of support. The authors state that as the study developed they became increasingly aware of the significance of efforts being made by voluntary and statutory agencies and, in particular, by local residents themselves, to develop systems of neighbourhood care, such as the so-called 'Good Neighbour Schemes' which formed the main focus for their research.

There is an important message here for those who plan and provide community care. They can be lulled by the cosy and comforting sound of the word 'community' into assuming that systems of support are in place when they may not be. Bulmer warns:

> *there are not (contrary to what some policy-makers seem to believe) informal social networks 'out there' waiting to be tapped ... traditional locally based social networks are in decline, and people's attachments are both more widely spread geographically and also to some extent more privatized within the nuclear family.*

> (Bulmer, 1987, p. 70)

On reading this section, one of our course testers told of how, when she was a young mother, her health visitor had put her in touch with another young mother with similar interests and living a similar lifestyle. The result has been a firm friendship that has survived 20 years. This, together with the support she got from other mothers at the local playgroup, kept her going. 'That introduction was the best thing a health visitor ever did for me', she said. Today there are many community-based initiatives in health and in social care that regard part of their purpose as strengthening or developing local communities, which may have been weakened by the effects of social and economic change. In the final section of the unit we shall be looking at some of these – starting with an account by a health visitor who changed her practice from working one-to-one to creating a group and listening to its needs.

Key points

- The idea that community is declining is probably broadly true but it is easy to overstate it.

- There is much variety in the extent to which people can call on local networks of support when they need care – important factors include people's lifestyle and the extent of their social and geographical mobility.

- The official policy of supplementing existing care networks assumes more community support than is often present.

- When assessing specific situations, care workers need to bear in mind varieties in communities and networks, and adjust care plans accordingly.

Section 4
Working with communities

The word 'community' is one that increasingly appears in job titles. Looking through job advertisements in recent newspapers, for example, I found:

- Development Officer, Scottish Community Development Centre: Community Health Network Project
- Community Development Officer, Cambridge City Council
- Welfare Rights/Community Worker, Saltley Action Centre, Birmingham
- Team Manager, Community Day Care, Solihull.

These examples start to demonstrate the sheer range of health and social care services that now claim the 'community' label. And it isn't only care services that are increasingly focusing on 'community'. From community police officers to community architects, it sometimes seems as though every profession is keen to stress its 'community' involvement. As Peter Willmott has said,

> Community ideas have gained momentum, over about a quarter of a century ... Now the word is everywhere, from community bookshops to community planning, from community broadcasting to community enterprise, from community transport to community dance.

> (Willmott, 1989, p. 1)

What does it mean for a service to be community based, and what are some of the key issues and problems involved in this kind of approach? In this section, we will be looking at some examples of community-based services from the fields of health and social care.

4.1 Health care and communities

Chapter 18 in the Reader, by Lyn Fisk, 'Housing primary health care in the community', provides an example of a service – in this instance health visiting – which set out to work closely with a particular local community in South Wales. It was part of the Teamcare Valleys Project, a programme sponsored by the Welsh Office to improve health in the valleys through supporting a wide range of health and social care practitioners and encouraging them to find new ways of working together. People on the estate where Fisk worked faced many of the problems associated with the widespread social and economic changes of recent years. In addition to the obvious signs of poverty and disadvantage, she refers to 'weak social support systems', a lack of communal facilities and an overall lack of a 'sense of commitment to the community'. The article describes the setting up of a drop-in centre on the estate – the Community Health House – which 'aimed to meet the wider health, social and personal needs' of women living on the estate. As Fisk makes clear, the project was part of a wider trend, in which health visitors, who have tended in the past to focus mainly on work with individuals and families, 'have been exploring different ways of working with groups and communities'. But what does this shift in emphasis entail?

Activity 10   **A health visitor and a community health house**

Allow about 20 minutes

Find Chapter 18 by Lyn Fisk in the Reader and read it now. When you have done so, jot down your answers to the following questions.

(a)   What are the features of a community-oriented approach to health care being used here? See if you can list three.

(b)   What are the main results of the survey of definitions of health among the potential users of the house?

(c)   What is the relevance of these findings to the community health role that the author is undertaking?

Comment   (a)   The three features of a community-oriented approach to health care that I picked out were these:

- it enables people to 'increase control over, and to improve, their health'

- it aims to 'promote skills, knowledge and confidence', rather than focusing on problems

- it sets out to 'validate, encourage and empower people to define and meet their own health needs', with the health worker acting as a 'facilitator'.

(b)   Crime and vandalism, lack of money and the poor state of the area are factors women in the sample most often cited as having a detrimental effect on their health. 'Good friends and neighbours' – in other words, supportive networks – in their view promoted their health. Clearly, then, the women have a broad definition of health – one that encompasses economic and social factors.

(c)   Fisk points out that this view of health is one that is shared by health workers who adopt a community development model.

Community development is an approach to work with local communities that has been employed in a wide variety of contexts, in both industrialised and developing countries. Andrew Glen sums up the goal of a community development approach as being 'to develop self-help and hence establish a sense of community principally, though not exclusively, on a neighbourhood basis' (Glen, 1993, p. 25).

A health visitor at work: recording a baby's progress

'Steps to Health' is a community-based health project, located in the Low Hill district of Wolverhampton. It has been set up, not inside the statutory health service or by NHS employees such as health visitors, but by the Wolverhampton City Challenge Partnership. However, it too adopts a community development approach in the sense in which Glen defines it. On Audio Cassette 3, side 1 you can hear two of the project workers, Janet Barlow and Mary Rose Lapin, talking about their work.

Activity 11 | **Introducing 'Steps to Health'**

Allow about 15 minutes

Switch on Audio Cassette 3, side 1 now, and listen to the first section, in which we hear Janet and Mary Rose describing the work of 'Steps to Health'. In Unit 12, we will be taking a closer look at the work of 'Steps to Health' with a community of gypsy travellers. Here, we are concerned primarily with the general approach to health work adopted by the project. When you have listened to the tape, make a note of what you think the two workers mean by a 'community development approach'.

Comment | The main element in this approach seems to be starting from the needs that local people themselves express, rather than imposing the workers' own agenda. In Janet's words: 'It's very much about starting by finding out what their agendas are, what their needs are, what their priorities are, and working on that'. But it also entails a particular approach to health, one that focuses on wider, environmental issues, rather than what Janet and Mary Rose call 'traditional health promotion issues'. In the case of the gypsy travellers, this meant concentrating (at least to begin with) on the pressing health problems caused by rats, drains and rubbish, rather than issues to do with smoking, eating and exercise.

The 'Steps to Health' workers identify a clash with what they call the 'traditional health promotion issues' represented by 'Health of the Nation' targets (see the box below). Lyn Fisk, too, points out tensions in community-based projects that adopt a wider view of health. She claims that there is a clash between this kind of definition of health and the way in which, traditionally, health services 'have been concerned with the provision of curative and preventative services rather than with seeking to influence the wider social and economic determinants of health'.

> **'The Health of the Nation'**
>
> *The Health of the Nation* was the title of a White Paper (Department of Health, 1993) presented to Parliament by the then Secretary of State for Health, Virginia Bottomley, in July 1992. The paper, which sets out 'a strategy for health in England', contains a number of key 'targets'. For example:
>
> - to reduce the prevalence of cigarette smoking in men and women aged 16 and over to no more than 20 per cent by the year 2000
> - to reduce the average percentage of food energy derived by the population from saturated fats by at least 35 per cent by 2005.

Fisk says that changes in the organisation of the NHS in the 1990s may have heightened this contrast, and she points to possible problems for the health visitor 'who has to mediate between the two views held by the community and the health trust'. She gives the example of 'an afternoon spent out in the fresh air picking strawberries', which may be perceived as more beneficial in health terms by women on a poor estate than a home visit by a health visitor, but which it may be difficult to justify to a manager concerned with resources and health gain targets. Equally difficult to justify in terms of the official targets would be work that the health visitor did in bringing together women in similar situations and helping them to form friendships and to offer each other mutual support.

You may recall a discussion of the limits of the biomedical model of health in Unit 2. There, a similar contrast was found between a traditional 'medical' model of health, which focuses on individual pathology, and what Fisk describes as a 'client-led' approach, which looks at wider causes and solutions.

Finally, Fisk describes the importance in the Community Health House of having 'a multidisciplinary team ... to provide support and activities', and she lists the wide range of statutory and voluntary agencies and workers involved in the project. Working across professional boundaries seems to be another key feature of a community-oriented approach.

Key points

• A community-oriented approach to health care aims to enable individuals and groups to define and meet their own health needs. It focuses on broad social and environmental factors rather than on people's behaviour and lifestyle.

• Such approaches have been used by voluntary sector projects, and in the NHS they can involve new ways of interprofessional working as well as new relationships between workers and clients.

4.2 Social work and communities

Where does a community focus fit in relation to social work? There were two main influences towards more of a community approach in social work in the 1970s and 1980s, namely the Seebohm report (Seebohm, 1968) and the Barclay report (National Institute for Social Work, 1982). The Seebohm report (implemented in the Local Authority Social Services Act of 1970) meant an important organisational change. It ushered in large-scale local authority social services departments that brought together the previously separate social work specialisms of mental health, work with children, and so on. The vision was of 'generic' social workers – in other words, social workers who worked with a range of clients, rather than focusing on a particular specialism – decentralised services, an accessible local office and the possibility of community involvement in the nature and extent of services offered. The Barclay report, coming just over a decade later, pointed in a similar direction, arguing that there had been too much emphasis on individual casework. It offered a vision of social workers who had a working knowledge of their local communities, who would be able to utilise and strengthen the formal and informal networks that existed locally, and who could work in a preventive way to support individuals, families and groups. The report talks of how:

> *Clients, relations, neighbours and volunteers become partners with the social worker in developing and providing social care networks*

and it says that the function of social workers is:

> *to enable, empower, support and encourage, but not usually to take over from social networks.*

> *(National Institute for Social Work, in Bulmer, 1987, p. 9)*

Yet while this kind of thinking generated enthusiasm in social work and a range of new community projects, it also proved controversial. First, social workers questioned whether such approaches were undermining their core skills of professional casework with individual clients. Second, there were criticisms that the community agenda aligned them too closely with left-wing agitation for resources to regenerate communities. Third, they faced dilemmas about whether an approach that entailed working with and empowering communities did not cut across their statutory responsibilities. It is this third question that I will examine below.

Social workers have a number of 'statutory' tasks – duties enshrined in legislation and designed to protect those who are vulnerable. A local authority may take into care a child who is considered to be in moral or physical danger. The social worker is involved in this. Also, under the relevant mental health legislation, a social worker may be involved in compulsory admission of an individual to hospital, where it is deemed that that individual is a danger to others or to him- or herself. Some of the tensions involved in being a statutory social worker based in the local community are brought out in the account overleaf by Linda, a social worker for many years in a small community in the centre of Glasgow. She begins by describing the community itself.

A social worker engaged in individual case work

The actual size of the 'community' I work in is really small. It's only seven streets actually, but it's got a very high proportion of what could be termed 'problem' families and the referral rate to our office is very high. The Housing Office wouldn't admit it, but I'm sure it's a bit of a dumping ground. I certainly don't know any families that are glad to live here.

It's a very enclosed group of streets. There's a railway line blocking them in and a huge factory complex surrounded by barbed-wire at the other end. There's really only one way in and one way out. No one from any of the services ever takes their car in, and that includes delivery vans or taxis. It's just known as not being wise.

There's no shops open now there. There was a corner shop run by an Asian family for a while but it ended up looking like a prison. The owners had to cage themselves in and they had one of these entry systems at the door so that you couldn't just walk in. It closed after a while. There's no other services at all there. No doctors, dentist, churches, even. And nothing at all for the kids. Not even a couple of swings or any grassy areas. Everything is outside of the estate.

Having set the scene in this way, she goes on to reflect on the way in which she works and describes how her thinking changed.

It's hard to say how I feel about working there. There's a kind of acceptance that social workers are there a lot. It's part of the culture. I don't think we've moved very much away from being 'the cruelty'. People aren't friendly and I can't say anyone is exactly pleased to see me but I'm not as frightened as you might imagine. In the years I've been there I've only had two incidents of being threatened. Once someone set their dog on me ... but it only barked and growled and another time a group of people from a top window threw eggs at me! But it's all reactive stuff I do, you know. We respond to situations of risk for children and also have a lot of children we're keeping a pretty close eye on. It wouldn't be right for me to get 'friendly' with families I work with. I never know when I might be in serious conflict with them over, say, a child protection issue. It's only fair that they know I'm from authority. I learnt that lesson the hard way. When I was very new I tended to want to make friends with families. It doesn't work. I once had a family I used to pop in for a cup of tea with. Then one day I had to call round and tell them there had been a phone call from the school saying their boy had said his dad had burnt him with cigarettes on his back and that they'd seen the marks. They felt let down and abused by me and they were right. I hadn't been clear with them about my role. I haven't done that again.

*I've realised now my role is one of quite a lot of assessment and control and even so I don't know if we do much more than keep the worst at bay. These families have multiple problems – poor housing, poor health, no facilities, drug and alcohol abuse, unemployment. In fact, I'm amazed and impressed that some of the families **do** manage and indeed flourish if not prosper!*

Activity 12   **On being a social worker with statutory responsibilities**

Allow about 10 minutes   Read the second part of Linda's account again. What is the main tension she identifies in being a local authority social worker working with a local community?

Comment The main tension mentioned by Linda is between a desire to get to know people in the community on a friendly basis, and her role as someone 'from authority' with a role that is focused on 'assessment and control', which may bring her into conflict with people she has become friendly with. From what she says, Linda seems quite sympathetic to the plight of people in the area, but feels it would be unfair to get too close to local people.

Does the fact that social workers have a statutory role that involves assessment and control inevitably cut across a community approach? Sibeon (1991), who has reviewed a number of studies in this area, argues that this is not the case. He refers to several projects that demonstrate that social workers can fulfil their statutory duties at the same time as moving towards a preventive approach based on closer involvement with clients. He also points out that not all social workers are statutory social workers in the sense described, and that much of the work that social services departments do is not professional social work but the provision of 'basic social services' and social care to a wide range of people. In his view, one component of social work – the part concerned with assessment and control – should not be allowed to shape the whole of a social worker's activity.

In her book *Learning to be Strong* (Whalley, 1994), Margy Whalley describes the part played by community social workers in setting up the Pen Green Centre for Under-5s and their Families in Corby, Northamptonshire, in the 1980s. Like Fisk, Whalley emphasises the importance for successful community-based initiatives of multidisciplinary working. The centre only came into existence because of a collaboration between health, education and social services, and was set up to be run by 'a single multi-disciplinary team under one manager' (Whalley, 1994, p. 2). Whalley describes the crucial role played in the process by community social workers:

> *In April 1982 in Northampton, a community social worker carried out a comprehensive data review and questionnaire, had discussions with professional workers and made visits to other centres of interest. At the same time in Corby, the community social worker worked with and listened to local families and helped set up a community action group.*
>
> *(Whalley, 1994, p. 3)*

Activity 13 **Varieties of social work activity**

Allow about 5 minutes How does the description of the community social worker's role in the extract from Whalley's account differ from Linda's description of her role?

Comment The main difference lies in the relationship between the social worker and members of the local community. Where Linda had to maintain a certain distance from people because of her role in relation to child protection, the community social worker actively set out to make contacts with and consult local families.

The social worker's role in helping to set up a community action group in this instance also points to another difference. The community served by the Pen Green Centre had grown up around the steel industry, which at one time attracted workers to Corby from as far away as Scotland. In 1980 the British Steel Corporation closed the steel works in Corby. In Whalley's words, 'The "Corby Candle" was a bleeder which burnt off

Pen Green Estate, Corby   *The Pen Green Centre*

excess gases produced during the steelmaking process and it was visible for miles around. When it finally went out, it marked the end of the steel working community' (Whalley, 1994, p. 7). Through their work in the area, the local social services team identified a number of key issues for the community:

> *Social workers had many concerns in the early eighties about a local housing policy which had resulted in many 'families with problems' being placed on one estate. They described the community as a 'ghetto community of the elderly and the poor'. They also noted that there was a low uptake of existing welfare and support services. Local people seemed unwilling or unable to use what was on offer in the town centre ... There were few local facilities for women with children.*
>
> *(Whalley, 1994, p. 8)*

The problems identified here are reminiscent of those experienced by people on the estate where Lyn Fisk worked as a health visitor. Nor are they dissimilar to the problems noted by Linda in her description of her social work 'patch' in Glasgow. However, a key difference is that, in Margy Whalley's account, the community social workers in Corby were able to intervene to address these underlying problems – for example, by setting up a community action group – rather than relating only to individuals. As a result of their consultation with local people, the community social workers were able to 'inform our decision-making and our practice with the views and expressed needs of local families':

> *We responded to ideas that professional colleagues identified as important and filled in the gaps which parents made us aware of, such as: responding to children with special needs during the holidays; offering children and their families a chance to get out and about in the minibus on day trips and residential holidays; providing adult community education services that were acceptable to local people; and by re-introducing localised health services inside the under-5s' centre. To have concentrated exclusively on setting up a quality nursery without this kind of knowledge of the community would have been a fundamental mistake.*
>
> *(Whalley, 1994, p. 10)*

The relationship between activities of this kind and conventional social work may seem as tenuous as that between strawberry-picking or making introductions between young mothers and traditional ideas of health care. Both of the examples I have concentrated on – the Community Health House and the Pen Green Centre – adopt what we might describe as a holistic approach, focusing on the needs of groups and communities, and seeking to address the wider, social and environmental causes of the problems faced by individuals.

What of today – when both health and social care workers are operating in the world after the 1990 NHS and Community Care Act? Malcolm Payne, writing about social work and community care, takes the line that recent policy developments 'represent a move away from commitment to community and collective responses to social need towards individualisation' (Payne, 1995, p. 32). Payne also describes health and social services as 'two empires ... both with an interest in care and treatment, each separately managed, and both with a role to play' (p. 38). How overlaps and joint functioning will be handled in future is an open question. One thing that both 'empires' share, however, is a strand of thought which regards 'the community' not only as the setting in which their services take place, but as a resource that can be used to strengthen and develop the caring services that they offer.

In summary, then, while the word 'community' in job titles may be overworked and in some cases may not mean a lot, community-oriented initiatives are an important strand of work in health and social care. Debate will probably continue about the balance between individual and collective approaches, both in professions such as social work and health visiting and in relation to the needs of different service users.

A community approach to meeting local needs: Pen Green Centre, Corby

---

Key points

- Community social work emphasises starting from local people's needs and working with local networks. It takes a wider, environmental view of social needs.

- Community approaches in health and social care share some common assumptions and ways of working. As yet, though, they are not closely linked to each other.

- Social workers themselves have debated the importance of community approaches in social work.

- One controversy concerns social workers' statutory responsibilities and what these imply for community working.

- Overall, however, community building can be seen as a resource to strengthen and develop caring services in both health and social care.

As a final activity for this unit, you are asked to look at the chapter by Marjorie Mayo, in the Reader. Entitled 'The shifting concept of community', it is a wide-ranging review of the idea of community and its many uses by a variety of commentators.

Study skills: Extending your reading range

It is always difficult to get to grips with the literature in a new area of study. It's like trying to join in a conversation that has been going on for ages. You don't know what questions have been asked or what answers have already been given. To make matters worse, specialised language is used. At first you just have to 'hang in there' and try to pick up what is going on. In K100 we have generally chosen readings that are not highly specialised. However, you will eventually need to become comfortable with the mainstream writing in the field, and the Mayo article gives you a chance to practise. You already know some of the content from your reading of Unit 11. Just see what you can get from it, and don't worry if you can't make sense of every bit.

Activity 14   The 'shiftiness' of community

Allow about 20 minutes   Read Chapter 12 by Marjorie Mayo in the Reader now. Can you see where
     the points it makes are similar to the themes of this unit, and can you see where it differs?

Comment   Mayo's discussion is not easy to follow if you are still at an early stage of understanding ideas in this area. You should not be concerned if you feel you do not understand it fully. Points that may have occurred to you, however, include the following.

1   Mayo takes a broader historical sweep than I have done in this unit. She goes back to the fourteenth century and traces different meanings of the concept of community over time.

2   She assumes a knowledge of sociology and of Marxist ideas and relates to these more closely than I have done.

3   Nevertheless, her argument, as here, stresses the nostalgia factor in concepts of community and makes similar distinctions between community as place and community as interests.

4   She summarises the arguments of Bulmer, a key writer whom I have also relied upon.

5   She discusses the dynamics of change in communities and singles out, again as I have done, the position of women in relation to arguments about community.

6   Although the extract you have in the Reader does not go on to examine policy implications in detail, it is clear that Mayo sees these as important. As a key quotation, I would single out the passage where she says:

it is clearly highly relevant in policy terms for community care to know to what extent community ties still persist, or could at least be revived, to provide informal caring ...

Conclusion

In this unit, you have seen how both policy and practice appeal to powerful shared ideas about community, and particularly the ideal of the close, caring community. Returning to the core questions set out at the beginning of the unit, we can say that people mean very different things when they talk about community, but in the main, community is used as a positive word conjuring up forms of warmth, caring and concern for others which may – or may not – be available in the local settings in which people live. We often refer to localities when using the word 'community', but communities of interest and networks of support are important too. One of the major changes may well be that many people now rely less on a geographically bounded community and more on networks of support involving family, friends and support groups of different kinds. However, changes such as these have affected different groups in society in different ways. Care is available through the many networks in which people participate, but those who design and deliver services need to take account of the variety of communities and in some cases of the absence of community support. People working in health and in social care may be involved in community initiatives. Health and social care staff working in a community-oriented way share a common aim of strengthening and developing a sense of community, starting from local people's expressed needs and adopting a social and environmental approach to health and care needs. Such approaches need to be seen alongside services to individuals, as part of the overall set of services that can be designed to help us care for ourselves and for each other.

Unit 12 will take the idea of community further and will examine the challenges to health and social care services that come from acknowledging diversity and difference within and between communities, particularly those that represent ethnic diversity, and devising ways to respond to the variety of care needs that people have, both individually and collectively.

Study skills: Tackling the assignment

Now you are halfway through Block 3, how are you shaping up to your next assignment? With two blocks' worth of experience behind you, what have you learnt about the writing process? In fact, how has the essay writing gone generally? Have you found it a struggle to get your ideas together and get the writing done? Did it turn your week upside-down? Were you a pain to family and friends?

Did reading the first three sections of Chapter 6 of *The Good Study Guide* in Block 2 help? Did you find you could break the essay work into stages, as suggested, and work on them a bit at a time? How will you organise your work on TMA 03? Why not try jotting down a plan of attack now, and then see whether you can stick to it.

Study diary

You could include this reflection on essay writing as part of bringing your study diary up to date.

References

Atkinson, D. (1994) *The Common Sense of Community*, Demos, London.

Baldock, J. and Ungerson, C. (1994) *Becoming Consumers of Community Care: Households within the Mixed Economy of Welfare*, Joseph Rowntree Foundation, York.

Bulmer, M. (1986) *Neighbours: The Work of Philip Abrams*, Cambridge University Press, Cambridge.

Bulmer, M. (1987) *The Social Basis of Community Care*, Allen and Unwin, London.

Coates, K. and Silburn, R. (1970) *Poverty: The Forgotten Englishmen*, Penguin, Harmondsworth.

Dean, M. (1997) 'Tipping the balance', *Search*, 27, Spring.

Department of Health (1993) *The Health of the Nation: A Strategy for Health in England* (White Paper), HMSO, London.

Fryer, P. (1984) *Staying Power: The History of Black People in Britain*, Pluto Press, London.

Gavron, H. (1966) *The Captive Wife*, Penguin, Harmondsworth.

Glen, A. (1993) 'Methods and themes in community practice' in Butcher, H., Glen, A., Henderson, P. and Smith, J., *Community and Public Policy*, Pluto Press, London.

Jeavans, C. (1997) 'Love thy neighbour', *The Big Issue*, March, p. 12.

Lewis, J. (1992) *Women in Britain since 1945*, Blackwell, Oxford.

McNamee, P. and Lovatt, T. (1987) *Working-Class Community in Northern Ireland*, Ulster People's College, Belfast.

Morrison, B. (1997) *As If*, Granta Books, London.

National Institute for Social Work (1982) *Social Workers: Their Roles and Tasks* (Barclay report), NISW/Bedford Square Press, London.

Payne, M. (1995) *Social Work and Community Care*, Macmillan, London.

Seabrook, J. (1984) *The Idea of Neighbourhood: What Local Politics Should Be About*, Pluto Press, London.

Seebohm, F. (1968) *Report of the Committee on Local Authority and Allied Personal Social Services* (Cmnd 3703), London, HMSO.

Sibeon, R. (1991) *Towards a New Sociology of Social Work*, Avebury, Aldershot.

Snaith, R. (ed.) (1989) *Neighbourhood Care and Social Policy*, HMSO, London.

Townsend, P. (1957) *The Family Life of Old People*, Routledge & Kegan Paul, London.

Whalley, M. (1994) *Learning to Be Strong: Setting up a Neighbourhood Service for Under-Fives and their Families*, Hodder and Stoughton, London.

Willmott, P. (1967) *Consumer's Guide to the British Social Services*, Penguin, Harmondsworth.

Willmott, P. (1989) *Community Initiatives: Patterns and Prospects*, Policy Studies Institute, London.

Willmott, P. and Young, M. (1960) *Family and Class in a London Suburb*, Routledge & Kegan Paul, London.

Young, M. and Lemos, G. (1997) 'Roots of revival', *Guardian*, 19 March, 1997, pp. 2–3.

Young, M. and Willmott, P. (1962) (first published 1957) *Family and Kinship in East London,* rev. edn, Pelican, London.

Acknowledgements

Grateful acknowledgement is made to the following sources for permission to reproduce material in this unit:

Text

p. 80: Rosser, N. (1997) 'If you see anything you keep your mouth shut', *Evening Standard*, 12 May 1997, by permission of Solo Syndication, photographs © The Marquess Estate and Bruno Cattini.

Illustrations

p. 61: Peter Marshall/Photofusion; *p. 63 (left)*: cover of Townsend, P. (1957) *The Family Life of Old People*, Penguin Books Ltd, photographs courtesy of Emeritus Professor Peter Townsend; *p. 63 (middle)*: cover of Willmott, P. and Young, M. (1967) *Family and Class in a London Suburb*, Penguin Books Ltd, courtesy of Penguin Books Ltd; *p. 63 (right)*: cover of Young, M. and Willmott, P. (1962) *Family and Kinship in East London*, Penguin Books Ltd, photograph courtesy of Hunstein; *p. 68*: cover of Coates, K. and Silburn, R. (1975) *Poverty: The Forgotten Englishmen*, Penguin Books Ltd, courtesy of Penguin Books Ltd and Roger Mayne; *pp. 71 and 84 (left)*: Steve Eason/Photofusion; *p. 77*: Crispin Hughes/ Photofusion; *p. 83*: C. Stadtler/Photofusion; *p. 96*: Tomas Carter/ Photofusion; *p. 99*: N. Johnston/Photofusion; *pp. 102 and 103*: Pen Green Centre.

Unit 12
Communities, Diversity and Care

Prepared for the course team by Martin Robb with Linda Jones

While you are working on Unit 12, you will need:
- Course Reader
- Offprints Book
- Audio Cassette 3, sides 1 and 2
- Block 2, Unit 8

Contents

Introduction

Living in the same place does not necessarily create a sense of community among the inhabitants of an area, as you saw in Unit 11. The population of a local area may be made up of people with a variety of lifestyles and interests, and we noted that many people identify as much (or more) with the 'communities of interest' they belong to, as with the geographical area where they live. Communities of interest may be temporary – we mentioned campaigning groups and groups that have a particular leisure interest in common. But we also identified longer-term attachments based, for example, on religious belief or ethnic origin, that is to say, belonging to a group with a shared culture. Sometimes communities of this kind overlap with communities of place – examples are areas of Belfast which are predominantly Catholic or Protestant, or parts of Bradford which have been settled by Asian Muslims. Elsewhere, local areas will include people who identify with a wide range of communities of interest.

In Unit 11 we noted that applying the word 'community' to a group of people can be a means of distancing oneself from their experience. Terms like 'the black community' or 'the Asian community', and even more vaguely, 'minority ethnic community' are useful as shorthand, but they can also be used to suggest that people within the group are 'all the same' – and at the same time 'not like us'. In Unit 3 you met an article by Jenny Morris, writing as a physically disabled person, that challenged this kind of *labelling* of groups of people as 'different' from the mainstream. In this unit, we will be exploring how this process can influence the ways in which members of minority ethnic groups experience care services.

This unit sets out to explore the implications for health and social care services of acknowledging the diversity of ethnic groups to be found in Britain today. As you will see, there are many such groups whose experience we could consider. For this unit, I have necessarily had to make a selection. There has been a growing amount of research on questions of ethnicity and culture in the health and social care services, and an important role has been played by voluntary projects and by grassroots initiatives from within minority ethnic groups. Here we will be focusing on services for four main groups – gypsy travellers, Asian women, African-Caribbean families, and the Jewish community. Wherever possible, both on the audio cassette and in the evidence from research, we use the voices of people from minority ethnic groups themselves.

In the first section of the unit we consider the notion of 'diversity' and challenge the popular idea that the variety of traditions and cultures to be found in the UK is a recent phenomenon. We then move on to look at the relationship between ethnic differences and people's experience of health and social care services, and place these in the context of prejudice and discrimination. Finally, we explore how health and social care workers can help minority groups to gain access to appropriate care and support, and consider examples of imaginative and innovative service provision to meet their needs.

Core questions

- What experiences do members of minority ethnic groups in the UK today have of health and social care services?

- What kinds of factor influence their experience of health and social care services?

- What can providers of services do to ensure that all groups in the community have equal access to appropriate care?

Section 1
Community and diversity

In Unit 11 you saw how nostalgia for an imagined 'golden age' of community has influenced thinking about community in the present, and how these ideas have helped to shape policy and practice in health and social care. A key element in the myth of 'community past' is the belief that people used to live in harmonious local communities, united by common values and taking part together in a regular round of shared rituals and customs – in other words, that local communities were once united by a common *culture*. We can see this idea reflected in media images, such as nostalgic television advertisements which feature rosy-cheeked boys cycling through village streets of friendly, well-fed people, or families gathered by the fireside in cosy farmhouses. The former prime minister John Major appealed to such nostalgic ideas when he conjured up his vision of a Britain typified by warm beer, cricket on the village green, and old maids cycling through the morning mist to Holy Communion. As you saw in Unit 11, images of this kind are often invoked by those who lament the apparent 'decline' of community in support of calls for a 'return' to communities of this kind.

But such images are as interesting for what they leave out as for what they include. They present a picture of Britain that is overwhelmingly rural and English, largely Christian (more particularly Anglican), and often middle class. The experiences of city-dwellers, for example, or people living in Scotland, Wales and Northern Ireland, as well as working-class people and those from different religious or cultural traditions, tend to be absent from these idealised images of British life. Such images subordinate the immense variety of people's experiences to an imaginary 'norm' of Britishness.

As well as overlooking diversity of experience based on regional and class differences, images of community of this kind gloss over the *ethnic* diversity that has long been a feature of British experience. Social scientist David Mason reminds us that the population of the UK has always been mixed and has changed over the generations. 'The British population was the result of successive migrations from earliest recorded history and resulting from impulses as diverse as conquest and religious refugeedom' (Mason, 1995, p. 21). The 'British people', he argues, have been formed by the inward migration of, among others, Celts, Romans, Saxons and Normans. In addition, there have always been significant minority ethnic groups within Britain. In Young and Willmott's study (1962), the population of Bethnal Green included large numbers of descendants of French Huguenot refugees, while the East End of London as a whole became home for many groups of political and economic refugees – particularly Jewish refugees – from Europe during the late nineteenth and early twentieth centuries (Mason, 1995). The same period saw the beginnings of the growth of a significant Irish community in Britain: 'A combination of poverty, famine, and population growth in Ireland ... and labour shortages in the British economy led to the development of a pattern of migration which persists up to the present day' (Mason, 1995, p. 21). More recently, migrants have come to Britain from Commonwealth countries, although it is important to recognise that there have been people of African and Asian origin living in Britain since at least the sixteenth century (Fryer, 1984).

Modern Britain: a diverse society

All of this indicates that ethnic diversity is a consistent feature of British life. National populations are always changing, and there has always been migration to and from, as well as within, the British Isles. In the three decades after 1950, for example, migration out of the UK was significantly higher than inward migration (Layton-Henry, 1984). Migrants went to Commonwealth countries and to mainland Europe. The inward migration came from former colonies, particularly in the Caribbean and South Asia, and was stimulated by the break-up of the British empire and strong demands in the UK for labour in the post-war period. The extent of this inward migration should not be exaggerated. The 1991 census showed that people who were defined as being of non-white origin represent about 5.5 per cent of the British population, or around 3 million people in total (Mason, 1995). Of these, over half were born in the UK. White ethnic minorities are much more difficult to identify in the census, but one of the largest minority ethnic groups in England and Scotland is made up of people of Irish origin.

A note on terminology

There is a good deal of confusion about the terms used to refer to the different groups that make up the British population. Part of the problem is that many of the terms in everyday use have been used vaguely, or misused to bolster negative views of minority groups. The terms 'race' and 'racial' , for example, will not generally be used in this unit. They have become discredited by research which has shown no essential differences between racial groups, and by their association with ideas of racial superiority. Although the terms 'ethnic' and 'ethnicity' can also be misused, their advantage, says social policy researcher Linda Jones, is that they do not imply biological differences between groups of people:

> *Ethnicity refers to cultural practices and outlooks that characterise a given group of people and distinguish them from other groups. The population group feels itself, and is seen to be, different, by*

> *virtue of language, ancestry, religion, a common history and other shared cultural practices – such as dietary habits or style of dress. Ethnic differences, in other words, are wholly learned; they are the result of socialisation and acculturalisation, not of genetic inheritance.*
>
> *(Jones, 1994, p. 292)*

So differences between ethnic groups are the result of shared history and experience. And, of course, everyone belongs to an ethnic group, including those who see themselves as part of the majority population.

Another term to be clear about at the start is *racism*. This word is used by minority ethnic groups themselves and by researchers to refer to the whole range of unfair treatment of people on racial and ethnic grounds. This might include *stereotyping* people – making generalised assumptions about them because they belong to a particular ethnic group. Stereotyping may also reflect *prejudice* – a generally negative attitude towards certain ethnic groups. Attitudes of this kind may lead to *discrimination* – treating people unfavourably, simply because they belong to a specific group. You will come across examples of all of these as you proceed through the unit, and you will find a more detailed discussion of prejudice, discrimination and racism in Section 3.3.

A close look at any local area will show the great variety of ethnic groups within the UK today, although this is more noticeable in some areas of the country than in others. Neelam Aggarwal, Director of the Multicultural Resource Centre in Northampton, described in an interview the range of ethnic groups in her town:

> *There is quite a good, rich mixture of different ethnic groups. In Northampton we have Gujerati Hindus, Hindu Punjabis, we have Punjabis, Sikhs, Bengalis, we have African-Caribbean people, we have Vietnamese, Chinese, a good strong Irish community, there is a Bahai community in Northampton, and of course the mainstream culture.*

Notice that some of the groups mentioned by Neelam share a common ethnic background, while others also share religious beliefs. The inclusion of the Irish community in the list is also a reminder that minority ethnic groups may include white groups. Finally, although Neelam adds that people belonging to 'the mainstream culture' are themselves an ethnic group, it is important to remember that there are differences of culture and belief *within* the so-called 'majority' community.

Activity 1   Diversity in your local area

Allow about 5 minutes   Think of your own local area, or one you have lived in recently, and list the range of ethnic groups it contains.

Comment   Here are contrasting comments from four testers of the course materials:

> 'I was amazed at what I found in my own locality. I hadn't realised the variety of cultures present. This activity opened my eyes!'

> 'My part of Wales is 100% Caucasian (white). In a recent discussion with primary school children here, it was found that most of them had never seen a black person, apart from on TV. England is viewed as a 'far off' land. However, we do have other types of cultural diversity in that some parts are nationalist and Welsh speaking and others aren't at all.'

> 'In mid Bedfordshire where I live it looks white but almost all the village shops are owned by Asian families and the larger villages have Indian and Chinese-run restaurants.'

> 'In my local area of Birmingham there are mainly white middle class families of English origin. But where my friends live ten minutes away the community is largely British-born Asian with a strong Muslim faith.'

Your own answer will depend, of course, on the part of the country where you live, whether it is an urban or rural area, and the history of migration to, from and within the local area. The minority ethnic population of Britain is comparatively small and very unevenly spread across the country. Although there are members of minority ethnic groups living in most parts of the country, the population is largely concentrated in England and, within England, is concentrated in the most urbanised and densely populated areas.

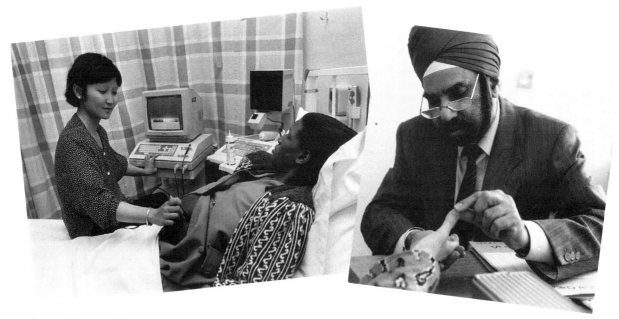

Workers and users of health and social care services reflect the diversity of modern Britain

As a consequence, can the needs and experiences of minority ethnic groups safely be ignored by people in other parts of the UK? This claim is sometimes put forward by service providers in areas where there are relatively small minority ethnic populations, who resist pressure to implement equal opportunities policies or training initiatives. Against this it can be argued that as geographical mobility increases there are very few parts of Britain unmarked by diversity of culture and traditions. Health and social care workers are themselves likely to move around the country during their careers and to encounter a range of cultures and minority ethnic groups. And the argument that awareness and understanding of diversity should be an integral part of being a citizen in the UK today is increasingly accepted.

Sometimes resistance to adapting to diversity is expressed in such terms as 'we don't have that problem here'. This is to view diversity as a threat or a problem. As Mason says:

> *Difference, particularly ethnic difference, has typically been seen as a problem in Britain. This is in part because of the tendency to assume that there was some primordial norm of Britishness from which newcomers, such as migrants, initially diverged but towards which they could ultimately be expected to change.*

(Mason, 1995, p. 2)

One consequence of this for policy and practice in health and social care is that minority groups may be viewed largely in terms of how they differ from the supposed 'norm' of British society. These differences are seen as causing 'problems' which will disappear when such groups assimilate into 'mainstream' British society. So the pressure has been to ignore or suppress difference. By contrast, Mason argues that we should accept and celebrate the wide variety of traditions, beliefs and values – 'the richness and complexity which is Britain in the 1990s' (p. 41). In this view health and social care agencies should take account of cultural diversity, rather than provide services that claim to be universal when in fact they reflect the needs and interests of the majority population.

This unit will be concerned with diversity mainly in terms of ethnicity and culture. Of course, the UK is diverse in other ways too. As noted in Unit 10, there are differences and inequalities in experience of health and social care services depending, for example, on people's social background, gender or lifestyle. In other units of the course, you will have become aware of the need for service providers to take account of other forms of diversity, including the needs of people who are disabled and those who are homeless – and of the ways in which these groups are stereotyped. Some of these aspects of diversity, as I shall note in passing, crosscut and reinforce ethnic difference. However, our task here is limited to focusing on one aspect of diversity – which will enable us to explore the nature of difference and inequality in greater depth. As you work through the unit, reflect on how the main points made here also apply to other kinds of diversity and difference.

Key points

- The UK today is characterised by a range of 'communities of interest', including many minority ethnic groups with distinctive traditions and values.

- Nostalgic ideas of community marginalise ethnic and cultural diversity.

- Welfare services need to take account of the diversity of the population, rather than assuming that everyone has the same attitudes, needs and experiences of health and social care.

Section 2
Culture and context

2.1 Customs and traditions

In this section we begin to explore the diversity of attitudes to, and experiences of, health and social care among minority ethnic groups. In Unit 11 you listened to the first section of the audio cassette for Block 3, in which you heard Janet Barlow and Mary Rose Lapin, of the Steps to Health project in Low Hill, Wolverhampton, discussing their work. In particular, they described their work with residents on a site for gypsy travellers in the area, including the formation of a residents' committee to campaign for healthier conditions on the site. The gypsy travellers represent a particularly striking example of a 'community of interest', marked out from the majority population and unified by distinctive traditions and ways of life.

Activity 2   **Gypsy customs and traditions**

Allow about 15 minutes

In the second section of Audio Cassette 3 (side 1), you will hear two of the gypsy travellers, Kathleen Hanrahan and Rita Lee, talking about their experiences, both of care within the gypsy community and of mainstream health and social care services. Listen to the whole of this section of the audio cassette now. As you listen, make a brief note of any customs or traditions mentioned by Kathleen and Rita that strike you as distinctive or different from those of 'mainstream' culture. (*Note*: 'Gorgio' is the term used by gypsies to refer to non-gypsies.)

Comment   These were my notes:

*   Customs to do with childbirth – other children put outside when baby born – women stay in bed for ten days until 'churched' (a traditional Christian ritual for 'purifying' women after childbirth).

*   Older people cared for at home, if possible – if have to go into hospital, not left on own.

*   Women don't work outside home after marriage – main role is to look after family and home.

The details of your own answer may have varied, depending for example on what you thought of as 'mainstream' culture. You may belong to, or have experience of, a group that has similar customs or traditions to the gypsies. However, I think you can see that the way of life among the gypsy travellers, as described by Rita and Kathleen, differs in a number of significant respects from that of the majority of people in the UK. A majority of women now work after marriage, for example, and many older people are cared for in residential homes.

Activity 3   **Gypsy values**

Allow about 5 minutes   A minority group's customs can tell us a good deal about the values and attitudes shared by people who identify with that group. Look back over the list you made. What kinds of attitude do you think they reflect?

Comment I thought that the practice of women not working after marriage reflected a 'traditional' division of labour between men and women. The survival of the custom of churching a woman after childbirth seemed to be another example of women's 'traditional' place in the community. Finally, the customs around the care of older people appeared to reflect a belief that it was the community's responsibility to care for its own, rather than relying on statutory or 'outside' care services.

What we are presented with here is a group with distinctive customs, reflecting attitudes to matters of health and social care which differ in many ways from those likely to be held by members of the wider population. We can see how these deep-seated attitudes influence the ways in which care is provided *within* the gypsy community. The attitude to older people, together with a view of caring as a woman's 'natural' role, for example, leads to a preference for providing informal care, where possible, rather than relying on outside agencies.

But how do their distinctive attitudes and values affect gypsy travellers' experience of statutory health and social care services? Do they make use of such services and, if so, what is their experience of using them?

A changing community: a permanent site for gypsy travellers

Activity 4 Experiences of health and social care services

Allow about 10 minutes Listen to the second section of Audio Cassette 3 again. Then note down answers to two questions:

(a) How do Kathleen and Rita describe their experience of statutory health and social care services?

(b) In what ways do you think this experience may have been shaped by gypsy customs and attitudes?

Comment (a) Rita and Kathleen mention a number of encounters with statutory health and social care services. As well as the reluctance to have older people cared for in hospital, they also talk about their experience of registering with a doctor. Although neither has had any recent difficulties, Kathleen mentions having some problems seeing a GP when she was travelling. Both women talk about the preference of gypsy women for a woman doctor and about some of the difficulties this presents.

(b)   In these examples we can see some apparent links between the
customs and attitudes noted earlier and the gypsy travellers'
experience of health and social care services. The value placed on
care by their own community can be seen as a factor in their
reluctance to use hospitals, while the 'traditional' divisions
between the sexes probably contribute to the reluctance by gypsy
women to be seen by a male doctor. More broadly, Kathleen's
experience while travelling seems to suggest that the gypsies'
itinerant way of life plays some part in their problems in gaining
access to services.

Is this the whole story, though? Are the gypsies' own customs and
attitudes the only factor shaping their experience of care services? At the
beginning of the audio extract, Rita and Kathleen describe encounters of
a rather different kind with members of the caring professions, when
they detail the assumptions that some workers, in particular teachers
and health visitors, have made about the gypsies.

Activity 5   Assumptions about gypsies

Allow about 5 minutes   Look back over your notes and, if necessary, listen to the cassette again.

Then write down what assumptions people tend to make about gypsies,
according to these accounts by Rita and Kathleen.

Comment   Rita's and Kathleen's view is that gypsies are seen as dirty by outsiders –
hence the schoolteacher's apparent surprise and sense of shame on
visiting Rita's trailer. They also feel that they are seen as incapable of
looking after their own children, and need to be taught how to sterilise
babies' bottles, and so forth. In fact, both assumptions appear to have
been untrue in this case. Rita's trailer was spotlessly clean and Kathleen
was clearly well aware of modern methods of feeding and caring for
babies.

These comments illustrate the complex relationship between cultural
differences and the experience of health and social care. For service
providers it may seem that the gypsies' cultural traditions are the major
problem. But for Rita and Kathleen it is the negative attitudes of the
service providers themselves that are crucial in determining gypsies'
experiences of care services. After all, the schoolteacher's stereotype of
gypsies as 'dirty' had influenced her judgement – until she saw Rita's
spotless trailer. Only then was she ashamed of (and presumably
questioned) her own assumptions.

Having learned the hard way that many outsiders are hostile to
gypsies, the gypsy women are, not surprisingly, defensive of their
way of life and sometimes suspicious of service providers. Course
testers commenting on this section of the audio cassette suggested that
this may have resulted in a misunderstanding of the health visitor's
role:

> '*Health visitors are specifically trained to check whether **all** their clients
> know how to sterilise a bottle. Checking whether these women know is
> just doing their job ...*'

> '*Health visitors that I have known who worked closely with gypsies
> have always liaised on behalf of the gypsies and built up a very close
> relationship with them. In the area where I live the gypsy mothers*

would often come to the Health Centre to find a health visitor to ask for help or advice ... In local arguments between the gypsies and local councillors and social services the health visitor has always been the gypsies' advocate ...'

In some health and social care encounters, service providers will resist stereotypes or set them aside as they come to understand different ways of life. As this happens, it will be easier for service users, such as Rita and Kathleen, to put aside their distrust of statutory services. However, in cases where providers do allow their preconceived, negative attitudes to influence their work, encounters will be marked by *prejudice* and *discrimination*. As you will see in the sections that follow, this can result in unfair treatment of minority ethnic groups.

Key points

- Gypsies, like other minority ethnic groups, have traditions and values which differ in some respects from those within 'mainstream' culture.

- A minority group's traditions and values play an important part in determining its attitudes to health and social care.

- Although traditions and values play some part in shaping people's experience of statutory welfare services, the attitudes and assumptions of outsiders, including care workers, are also of great importance.

Study skills: Voices as 'source material'

On Audio Cassette 3 you hear people from four different minority groups speaking at length. This presents quite a rare opportunity. How often have you listened to the views of gypsy travellers? Every day if you are a gypsy traveller yourself – but seldom, perhaps, if you are not. Although you live in a very diverse society, your personal life probably gives you contact with only a few sections of it. (Even if you meet a broad cross-section of people through your work, you are quite restricted in what you can talk to them about.) Of course you see and hear people from a range of different social groups on TV and radio broadcasts – yet that does not really put you in touch with the full breadth of society. Members of some groups appear very frequently through the mass media, but other groups are rarely represented – and when they do appear briefly, they are framed within programmes which ask particular questions and present particular 'angles', so you see and hear them in a very restricted way.

In other words, an audio cassette like this is a rather valuable resource. It enables you to hear voices directly – not interpreted by someone else with a point to make. You hear how other people view their circumstances and their lives – how they make sense of the world. It is very hard to acquire this depth of insight through print (except perhaps through novels), yet you pick it up very quickly as you listen. Of course, the speakers you hear are talking into a microphone, to an interviewer, with a sound recordist nearby – and they are answering questions – so it isn't 'normal conversation'. But they have enough time and scope to give a flavour of their particular way of looking at the world.

So the audio cassette is not simply 'more words to absorb'. It is *source material* for you to examine closely and think about. That is why we ask you to listen to it several times. You are listening not just to *what* is said, but also to what is *behind* the words – people's assumptions, attitudes, beliefs, ways of relating to society. You listen, not as a participant caught up in the emotions of a conversation, but as a detached 'observer' making a detailed analysis. (You could equally well analyse a recording of your own conversation with friends – there would be as much fascinating detail to uncover.) Social science enquiry often involves looking at very ordinary things in a lot of detail. It's what you look for and how you look that counts. The audio cassette activities above are an introduction to that kind of analytical approach.

2.2 The wider context

In what ways do attitudes towards minority ethnic groups influence the ways in which services are provided? To what extent do they lead to the provision of inferior services or unfair treatment?

Activity 6

A broader perspective on travellers' experiences

Allow about 15 minutes

Turn now to Offprint 17. The article, 'New ways' by Judy Hirst, is based on interviews with workers in projects with travellers, and was originally published in the journal *Community Care*. It gives an account of the changing experience of traveller communities, including gypsies, in Britain and the impact of these changes on their experience of care services. Read the article now and, as you do so, make a note of the examples it gives of travellers' experiences of health and social care agencies.

Comment

The article gives examples of travellers' experience of primary care services and social services. Hirst finds that the experience of many travellers in gaining access to primary health care is negative, with many GPs refusing to visit sites and many travellers unable to register with a practice. The result is that they often turn up repeatedly at accident and emergency departments for inappropriate reasons. This might have reminded you of the experience of Jim and Marianne in Unit 10.

The article quotes Karen McHugh, a worker with traveller communities in Harrow and Brent in London, who says that social workers often place traveller children on child protection registers needlessly, because they misinterpret aspects of the gypsy way of life. As a consequence, gypsies tend to be suspicious of social workers, seeing them simply as people who take their children away. (Perhaps this reminded you of the account in Unit 11 by Linda, the social worker in Glasgow, who said that people in her local community referred to social services as 'the cruelty'.)

The offprint also highlights the complex inter-relationship between outsiders' attitudes and gypsy culture. It suggests that gypsy culture, 'with its deeply religious, male-dominated rituals and mores' is very resilient to change, and there are suggestions that domestic violence is prevalent. Such features influence service providers' views of travellers and, in turn, the attitudes adopted by providers will influence travellers' access to and experience of health and social care.

At the same time, the offprint places these experiences in the context of the wider social and economic conditions which shape travellers' lives. The main focus is on the changes that in recent years have been forced on the estimated 60,000 to 100,000 travellers living in Britain.

Trapped by tradition – or victims of disadvantage? Travellers at a site on waste ground near Middlesborough

---

Activity 7   **The changing experience of traveller communities**

Allow about 5 minutes   According to Offprint 17, what have been the main changes affecting
   travellers in recent years? Have these changes improved or worsened conditions for them?

Comment   Hirst describes the economic and legal pressures which are forcing the traditionally nomadic travellers to adopt a more settled lifestyle, with growing numbers moving into permanent or temporary housing. The main change in the law affecting travellers' lives has been the Criminal Justice and Public Order Act 1994, which relieved local authorities of their duty to provide authorised sites, made it easier to evict travellers, and removed central government grants from local authority sites.

The offprint sees some positive benefits in these changes, in that they have made possible a closer relationship with welfare agencies in some areas – and the work of the Ealing Travellers Project is described in some detail. It is claimed that there have been particular benefits of this more settled existence for women and children in the traveller community. However, most of the consequences outlined in the offprint are negative. These include a lack of employment, since travellers are unable to move on and find work in their traditional trades. There is also evidence of overcrowding and worsening conditions on some sites, resulting in problems similar to those mentioned by Rita and Kathleen in the audio extract – such as rubbish and rats. The grim conditions at the Harrow site, for example, are said to be responsible for acute health problems, such as asthma and TB, as well as problems with alcohol and drugs, which can be seen as a consequence of these forced changes in the gypsy way of life. Examples are also given of travellers being harassed or denied access to local facilities, as well as being exploited by unscrupulous landlords.

The offprint indicates that the travellers' needs for health and social care services, and their experience of gaining access to those services, have to be viewed in the context of the wider social and economic disadvantages that they suffer. These disadvantages can be seen as resulting from widespread prejudice against travellers, which is reflected not only in the actions of individuals, but also in their treatment by statutory agencies, and indeed by the legal system.

Disadvantage and health inequality

Problems of disadvantage and inequality are not unique to gypsies, but are also shared by other minority ethnic groups and by low-income groups in the UK. Research has consistently shown the link between social inequality and inequality in health. Benzeval *et al.* (1995), for example, state: 'Across the developed world, no matter how social status is measured, those in the most disadvantaged circumstances suffer worse health than all of those above them, especially those who are most advantaged' (p. 1).

A 1995 Department of Health report on variations in health concluded that the health of professional groups (social class 1) was notably better than that of semi-skilled and unskilled workers (social classes 4 and 5). For example:

> *life expectancy at birth is currently around 7 years higher in the Registrar General's social class I than social class V*
>
> *children in social class V are four times more likely to suffer accidental death than their peers in social class I ...*
>
> *(Department of Health, 1995, p. 9)*

There is evidence that poverty and racism *act together* to increase health risks:

> *In general mortality rates for black and minority ethnic groups reflected their concentration in lower social classes and in semi-skilled and unskilled occupations, making them vulnerable to the health disadvantages associated with low income, poor housing and poorer health care facilities and access.*
>
> *(Jones, 1994, p. 306)*

A review of evidence on the health of the non-white minority ethnic population pointed to the possible effects of racism (Smaje, 1995). It suggested that the experience of racism may increase stress, producing physical outcomes such as raised blood pressure, and also operate as an underlying influence on people's health (this is a point I shall return to in Section 4). People who have experienced discrimination in housing, employment and other service provision will end up living in the most disadvantaged conditions, and the evidence linking social disadvantage and poor health is strong.

These comments helps us to put the role played by cultural differences in context. 'In any interpersonal contact', says Shama Ahmed, a social work education adviser, 'but especially in a therapeutic relationship, it is important to understand and acknowledge the cultural dimension.' She goes on: 'The awareness is important but it is not enough' (Ahmed, 1986, p. 140). Highlighting the significance of cultural differences in relation to health and social care should not distract attention from other factors shaping peoples' lives, such as poverty, unemployment or racism.

The complex role of culture

We need, then, to avoid quick judgements about the role of culture and ethnicity. For example, the tendency to see minority groups as responsible for their problems neglects the positive role that culture can play in the face of discrimination and disadvantage. There was an example of this in the conversation between Rita and Kathleen on the audio cassette. I said earlier that the traditional customs in the gypsy community, such as the ritual of 'churching' women after childbirth, appeared to reflect traditional, and fairly negative, attitudes towards women among travellers. But is this how the custom is viewed by the gypsies themselves?

Churching, the ritual purification of women in church after childbirth, used to be standard practice throughout European culture, but has virtually died out now. Traditionally, women were barred from activities such as food preparation until they had been churched, since the process of giving birth was thought to have made them unclean. Feminist writers, in particular, have viewed the custom critically and linked it to the inferior status accorded to women in the church and in the wider society. Perhaps you shared this view as you listened to Rita and Kathleen describing the custom?

However, in the context of the discrimination and disadvantages suffered by travellers, as well as the threats posed by enforced changes to their traditional lifestyle, it is possible to see the positive value of traditions that seem archaic and backward-looking to outsiders. The way in which the two women talk about the custom is overwhelmingly positive. Far from regarding it as demeaning, they interpret it as a sign of courtesy or respect for the woman, seemingly because it gives her a welcome break from cooking and other household duties. They also see the maintenance of the custom as a sign of respect for their elders and as a way of keeping up the traditions of a tight-knit community of interest. This is a warning against making judgements about customs and values without a consideration of the broader context in which people live their lives.

This section began by looking at the cultural traditions of one minority group and how these influenced their experience of health and social care. You have seen that the relationship between culture and care is more complicated than it may appear, and that supposed cultural differences cannot be understood outside the broader context of prejudice and discrimination experienced by many minority groups.

Key points

- More general kinds of social and economic disadvantage, as well as discrimination, create inequalities for minority ethnic communities.

- Cultural traditions and customs can be seen in a wider context as a source of strength and continuity for communities facing discrimination and disadvantage.

Study skills: What counts as evidence?

Much of the discussion in Section 2 has been based on reports of people's personal experiences (on the audio cassette and in the article from *Community Care*). The *value* of personal evidence of this kind, whether from users of services or care workers, is that it provides direct and engaging insights into first-hand experience. Listening to Rita and Kathleen talking about the rats and rubbish on their site communicates – in a way that a research report or an academic article could not – how it feels to live with such problems.

However, you need to bear in mind the *limitations* of evidence of this kind. Rita and Kathleen are two individuals – not a representative *sample*. They cannot speak for the whole gypsy community in Britain. The experience of other gypsy travellers may be very different. (You may have already noticed a difference between their experience of registering with a GP and that cited by Karen McHugh from her experience in Harrow.) This is not to say that the information they give is unsound: simply that it needs to be set alongside evidence from other sources and of other kinds – for instance in-depth interviews, or questionnaire surveys based on larger samples (some examples of which will be introduced later in the unit).

So, when you are assessing evidence from the personal experiences of a few individuals, you need to remind yourself that:

- it offers valuable *insights* into how people experience and understand the world, but

- it cannot be taken to be *representative* of the experiences of all members of the relevant group, so

- it needs to be set alongside *other kinds of evidence* which might support or challenge the insights offered.

Section 3
Working with cultural diversity

How should workers and service providers in health and social care respond to differences in customs and values that exist between ethnic groups? This is the main question that we will be exploring in this section, which focuses on the experience of a number of people of Asian origin living in Britain.

3.1 'We treat them all the same'

In the third section of Audio Cassette 3, you can hear Kalpana Desai, project co-ordinator of Dostiyo, an Asian women and girls' welfare organisation in Northampton. She describes the organisation's work and discusses the experience of Asian people generally, and of Asian women in particular, in gaining access to appropriate health and social care services.

Activity 8   **Asian people and access to services**

Allow about 20 minutes

Listen to the whole of the third section of the audio cassette now (it starts on side 1 and continues on side 2).

(a)   As you listen make a note of any examples Kalpana cites of Asian people being denied access to appropriate health and social care services.

(b)   Why does Kalpana think the services are not being used by these groups?

Comment   (a)   Kalpana says that the 'common issue' in Dostiyo's work is 'access to services and access to facilities'. The two main examples that I noted where access was denied relate to Bangladeshi women and to older Asian people. Kalpana says that the Bangladeshi women's needs are greater than those of some other Asian groups, because most of them have arrived in the country very recently and don't speak English. Since their husbands tend to work long hours, the women are on their own at home most of the time and in need of support. At the same time, Kalpana says that there is an existing mother and toddler group in the local school which might provide help, but that 'it's not accessible'.

Kalpana also describes the problems that older Asian people in Northampton have with using the meals-on-wheels service, and the problems for older Asian women in particular in making use of the existing day care facilities.

(b)   In describing the mother and toddler group, Kalpana says that there is no one there who speaks Bengali, and no one who understands the women, so they do not make use of the group. She also mentions the lack of information about facilities of this kind in a language or form that is accessible to the Bangladeshi women. With regard to the services for older people, Kalpana says that they are not 'culturally appropriate'. The meals-on-wheels service does not take account of the dietary needs of Asian people (the fact that Hindus do not eat beef, and in some cases are strictly vegetarian, for example, or that Muslims eat only halal meat), while the day centre seems to have no provision for the washing and toileting customs that are expected, particularly among older people (Hindus, for example, prefer to wash themselves with running water and prefer bidets to the use of toilet paper).

As Kalpana says, Asian elders are free to use these services, but it is clear that many of them feel disappointed and unhappy with what is on offer. The service providers appear either to be *unaware* of, or deliberately to *ignore*, the particular requirements of older Asian people. Yasmin Gunaratnam's research confirms that the problem is not confined to one part of the country. She quotes from Asian carers she interviewed in different parts of Britain:

> *He used to have meals on wheels, but even though it was useful to have them delivered, because they were so appallingly bad ... I don't think they had even heard of halal meat ... it was just a waste of money.*

> *I see some of the old people in this area, they just sit and look out of the window all day. They have no rights. No Asian people that I know go to day centres. People have nowhere to go. In the day centres there is no food for them, culture for them, music ... nothing ... so they just stay as they are – housebound.*

> (Gunaratnam, 1993, pp. 117–18)

In neither of these cases are Asian people *directly* denied access to services. There are no signs outside day centres in Northampton saying 'whites only', and the Bangladeshi women would not be turned away if they attended the existing mother and toddler group. However, these groups are *effectively* prevented from using the facilities because those providing the services fail to take account of their particular needs or to welcome them.

Properly provided for? Older Asians in Britain

These examples represent one kind of response to the question of how to treat cultural differences – and that is to ignore them. This approach is often defended on the grounds that the service is aimed equally at all groups in the population – 'we treat everyone the same' is a phrase that is often heard. For example, health services are termed universal services, providing the same service to everyone, regardless of their background. Wouldn't it be unfair to provide a 'special' kind of service to particular groups?

However, as these examples show, services that claim to be open to everyone, but fail to take account of the diversity of needs, actually reflect what are assumed to be the needs and culture of the majority population. A different way of thinking about what is meant by a universal service is needed – one that provides a diverse range of services to different groups.

Key points

- 'Treating everyone the same' can mean overlooking important cultural differences and denying access to services to minority groups.

- Being 'open to all' means taking account of the diversity of cultural needs among potential users of services.

3.2 'They look after their own'

Providing a fair and equal service also means basing decisions about health and social care provision on an informed understanding of cultural diversity, rather than on ill-informed assumptions.

On the audio cassette, Kalpana Desai describes some of the widespread misunderstandings about Asian family life, particularly the common assumption that *all* Asian people live in extended families which provide a network of care and support. One researcher, N.A. Patel, comments that: 'For a Black family (irrespective of 'ethnicity') the popular image is one of an extended family network, "families within families", providers of care and social and psychological support' (Patel, 1990, p. 30). However, the stereotype has been used particularly in relation to Asian families. 'Perhaps the most significant stereotype about Asian carers is that all Asian families live within an extended family, where roles and responsibilities are clearly defined and caring for ill or disabled family members is a "natural" function' (Gunaratnam, 1993, p. 115).

Kalpana Desai undermines this familiar stereotype. She notes that Asian family structures are changing, as are those in the rest of the UK population. According to Kalpana , the 'traditional' extended family is being supplemented, or replaced, by a wider range of family arrangements. In particular, the idea that all Asian elders are supported within large, extended families is becoming outdated, with some older people actually choosing to live on their own. Kalpana also makes the point that so-called extended families may need as much support as smaller, nuclear families.

A sequence of research studies has also challenged the myth of the extended family. As far back as 1981, Anil Bhalla and Ken Blakemore carried out a study of elders in minority ethnic groups in Birmingham and reported their own surprise at 'the finding that a quarter of the Asian elders have no close relatives in Britain ... given common ideas of the importance of the extended family in the care of Asian elders' (Bhalla and Blakemore, 1981, p. 33). A study of community services in Birmingham in the later 1980s revealed a significant mismatch between professional assumptions and Asian people's needs (Cameron *et al.*, 1989). Professionals assumed Asian families 'looked after their own' whereas Asian families actually did not know that services were available. More recently, Gunaratnam's research revealed:

> *a variety of relationships and patterns of care that included elderly couples living alone who were 'mutual' carers; elaborate systems of shared secondary care by relatives and friends living separately from the person*

*requiring care and single isolated carers whose relatives either were not
part of the family network or lived some distance away. In fact, only eight
out of the 33 carers interviewed lived in an extended family network.*

(Gunaratnam, 1993, p. 116)

Bimal Roy Bhanu, in a study carried out in the 1990s of the experience of
community care among the Mirpuri population in Middlesborough,
found that the stereotype of the extended family was still widespread,
despite their diversity of experience:

*The comments made by both carers and older people in interviews suggest
that, in practice, Social Services do not realise or accept that although
individual members of families may help with care responsibilities, this is
not done willingly, but due to a combination of traditional cultural values
of duty and obligation coupled with lack of other sources of help. The
carers more often than not, accept the role reluctantly and often require
significant help. Also, particularly among the Mirpuri community ...
because of the apparent lack of knowledge of services and representation of
needs, the individual falls into the trap of looking after the person
themselves.*

(Bhanu, 1996, p. 209)

In fact, Bhanu's interviews revealed 'that the majority ... of older people
and carers live in nuclear households, instantly undermining the belief
held by policy makers and welfare providers that extended families and
communal networks of informal care "look after their own" and don't
need services' (p. 210).

*Expected to 'look after their own': Asian families
in Britain*

The assumption that all members of Asian groups in Britain live in extended families is not only misleading: it can also have serious consequences. As Gunaratnam says: 'In many instances ill-informed assumptions about different minority communities have practically influenced policies and service provision' (1993, p. 115). Robina Shah offers an example from her own study of children with disabilities in Asian families: 'Parents were ... not offered services, on the assumption that they would not wish to utilise respite care or other support services because care would be within the family only' (Shah, 1992, p. ix).

Similar stereotypes, of families and communities able to 'look after their own', whatever the circumstances, are also applied to African-Caribbean people in Britain. A particularly tragic example of the consequences of basing practice on ill-informed stereotypes of this kind was the death of a black child, Tyra Henry, at the hands of her father, while legally under the supervision of Lambeth social services in south London. The report of the public inquiry into her death expressed concern about social workers' over-optimistic judgement of the ability of Tyra's grandmother, Beatrice Henry, to care for her:

> *Here was a woman, recently widowed, previously traumatised by the maiming and loss of a baby grandson, living on social security, with five children, in a grossly overcrowded flat and getting precious little financial or other help from her teenage daughters. It seems almost impertinent to ask how could she be expected to cope as Tyra's surrogate parent and first-line protector ...*
>
> *We believe that the assumption that Beatrice Henry would cope in the circumstances we have outlined was rooted in the perception of her as a type rather than an individual ... There is also a 'positive', but nevertheless false stereotype in white British society of the Afro-Caribbean mother figure as endlessly resourceful, able to cope in great adversity, essentially unsinkable. In it are both a genuine recognition of the endurance of Afro-Caribbean peoples in conditions of great hardship and an evasive and guilty recognition that many such people live in poverty in modern Britain.*
>
> *(London Borough of Lambeth, 1987, quoted in Gambe et al., 1992, pp. 108–9)*

Positive as well as negative assumptions about cultural differences can be misleading if they are based on inadequate information, and can have serious consequences.

Key points

- There is a widespread assumption that members of minority ethnic groups, and particularly members of Asian communities, live in extended families which provide extensive networks of care within the community.

- Research evidence shows that family arrangements in minority ethnic groups are actually extremely diverse and are changing in significant ways.

- The persistence of cultural stereotypes can lead to people being denied the care and support they need.

3.3 Stereotypes, prejudice and discrimination

Throughout this unit I have noted how cultural stereotypes, based on ill-informed assumptions about minority ethnic groups, can have an adverse impact on the delivery of services. In this section we are going to explore stereotyping, prejudice and discrimination in rather more depth.

Study skills: Honing your reading technique

How is your reading technique developing? Do you feel you are understanding enough, remembering enough, getting done quickly enough? In the next activity you will read another chapter from the Reader. How will you set about the task?

- Will you take a quick look through first to see what it seems to be about? Will you read just once, underlining key words as you go?

- How will you use the three parts of the activity? Will you have them on a piece of paper and write down answers as you come to them? Will you wait until the end to try to answer them? Will you ignore them?

- What notice will you take of the 30 minute target time? What if the article takes longer – will you stop at half an hour and just glance quickly ahead to check what the rest is about and then return to the unit? Will you see how interesting the reading is before deciding?

There are no 'correct' answers to these questions. You have to keeping asking yourself what works for you in the light of what you want out of the course. When you have finished the reading, come back to this box and check off what the answer turned out to be. Then think what you have learnt about your current reading technique.

Activity 9   Stereotypes of Asian families

Allow about 30 minutes

The chapter in the Reader by Robina Shah, '"He's our child and we shall always love him" – mental handicap: the parents' response', is based on Shah's research into the needs of children with disabilities in Asian families. In this chapter, Shah provides some examples of the kinds of assumption or stereotype about Asian women and Asian families that she has come across in her research work. She suggests that social workers' assessments may be based on ill-informed assumptions which misrepresent the realities of life for Asian families in Britain. Later, in the section headed 'Look behind the word Asian and see me', she lists further instances of stereotypical ideas of Asian parents' attitudes to disability.

Read Chapter 21 now. As you do so, note down your responses to the following:

(a)   What is your definition of stereotyping and why do people do it?

(b)   In Shah's view, what damage does stereotyping do to Asian parents?

(c)   In what way does Shah see a connection between ethnic stereotyping and racism?

Comment (a) Stereotyping means making broad, general assumptions about people, based on the social and cultural groups they belong to. It is sometimes claimed that stereotyping is an inevitable fact of life. It is certainly very difficult to avoid altogether. After all, none of us, whatever our own background, can have complete and detailed knowledge of every minority ethnic group in our society. Still less can we know the circumstances of the lives of every individual we have to deal with, in our work or other areas of our lives. Don't we need some kind of broad framework into which to 'fit' people, the details of whose lives may be, for the moment, hidden from us?

Working in health and social care often involves encountering large numbers of new people and making quick assessments of their needs based on limited information. In these circumstances, it is not surprising that people fall back on rough-and-ready generalisations, based for example on people's appearance, the way they are dressed, or the way they speak, and drawing on their own values, beliefs and norms of behaviour.

(b) Shah suggests that stereotyping can be very damaging. She points to some of the problems, for both users and providers of services, of relying on stereotypes as a guide to action. First, stereotypes are broad generalisations which overlook individual differences within communities, depriving people in Shah's words of their 'uniqueness'. As she says, Asian parents 'don't wish to be placed in the "pool of generalisations"' or have one person's experience 'speak for the whole Asian community'. Second, stereotypes tend to overlook similarities between ethnic groups and can lead to 'looking for differences where none exist'. Third, the process of stereotyping can lead to misinterpreting people's needs. An example Shah gives is the assumption that the absence of toys in the living room means that toys are not seen as important (this is reminiscent of Rita Lee's encounter with the health visitor).

(c) Shah places the process of stereotyping in the wider context of prejudice, discrimination and racism towards minority communities. She suggests that racism may be personal (the attitudes or actions of individuals) or institutional. If there is institutional racism the policies and practices of an agency discriminate systematically against black and minority ethnic groups, for example by denying them entry or blocking promotion.

The concept of *institutional* racism is an important, if controversial, one. It suggests that racism is widespread and deep-seated – not so much a matter of individual opinions as of practices embedded in organisations and structures, including those of health and social care services. Racism is not, Shah argues, simply the views and actions of a few individuals, but is deeply rooted in policies and practice – and in a society as a whole. Elsewhere in the book from which this chapter is taken, Shah traces the roots of racism towards black people in Britain's history:

> *Britain's imperialist history has an impact on both Black and White people today through its legacy of economic imbalances, unequal power relations and images of the colonised and colonisers. The slavery of the seventeenth, eighteenth and nineteenth centuries, although not principally accountable for racism, did give rise to the notion that Black people, who were bought and sold like cattle, were unable to be anything other than inferior to the White middle classes who owned them. Furthermore, since most slaves were Black, the colour of their skins became synonymous with negatives attitudes about their race.*

During the Victorian era an attitude of superiority towards Black people was fostered: the world was seen as being in racial strata, with white men holding the reins and promoting the perceived superiority of their civilisation. Even today those attitudes hold sway; Black people are less frequently in positions of management and, in spite of equal opportunities legislation and attempts at positive action, Black people are still overrepresented in the lower socio-economic groups.

(Shah, 1992, p. 3)

Although Shah's article and this unit focus on the experience of minority ethnic groups as *users* of services, it should not be forgotten that black and Asian people also face prejudice and discrimination as *workers* within health and social care services. You have already met an example of this at an individual level in Unit 1, in Lynne Durrant's racist attitude towards an Asian social worker. Evidence of widespread *institutional* discrimination against minority ethnic workers in statutory services has been found in a number of studies (Jones, 1994, pp. 319–21).

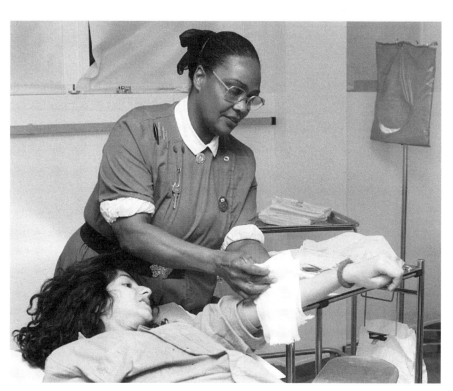

Equal opportunity? A black nurse in London

Key points

- Stereotyping – generalising about members of a particular group – can be seen as a natural, everyday process.

- However, stereotypes overlook individual differences and misrepresent the needs of members of minority ethnic groups.

- Stereotypes may be linked to prejudiced attitudes towards minorities, and may lead to discriminatory actions.

- Prejudice and discrimination have been seen as part of a wider pattern of racism, rooted in British history and reinforced by institutional power.

3.4 A clash of cultures?

Many of the stereotypes that exist about Asian communities focus on the place of women. As with the gypsy travellers, there is what Shah describes as a widespread 'assumption of male dominance' where women are forced to play a traditional, subservient role. Is there any truth in this stereotype, and what are the implications for work with Asian families?

Activity 10   Women in Asian communities

Allow about 15 minutes Listen again to the third section of Audio Cassette 3, which features Kalpana Desai. What examples are given here to support the conventional view of Asian men as having a conservative attitude towards women's roles?

Comment   Kalpana talks about frosty relations between Dostiyo and the male-led Asian organisations in Northampton, which she says have shown little support for their work with Asian women. She also mentions the cool response from these groups to Dostiyo's sexual health project, including a refusal to advertise its work. Kalpana and her colleague, Leila Abbass, say that many Asian women refuse to admit to being disabled because this is seen as reducing their value as 'commodities'. Finally, Dostiyo's work with young Asian women seems to provide evidence of the pressures imposed by 'traditional' community values – including the pressure to enter into arranged marriages.

Do these examples support the popular image of Asian culture? It is important to note that Kalpana says that Asian women share attitudes to disability with many other women; and Leila is at pains to point out that the supposed treatment of women as commodities occurs 'in some rural communities'. In other words we should be wary of stereotypes that ignore similarities with the treatment of women elsewhere or gloss over differences within a particular group. As Avtar Brah comments, it is easy to overlook the sheer variety of experience to be found among Asian women in Britain:

> *When we speak of South Asian women in Britain we are referring to a very heterogeneous category of people. Asian women have come to Britain from different parts of the world, most notably from India, Pakistan, Bangladesh, Uganda, Kenya and Tanzania. While those who have migrated from the Asian subcontinent are predominantly from the independent proprietor class of peasants, their counterparts from East Africa are overwhelmingly urban, middle-income families. Asian women are further differentiated according to religion, linguistic group, caste and sect. There are three major religions – Islam, Hinduism and Sikhism – and five major languages – Punjabi, Gujarati, Bengali, Urdu and Hindi – represented among Asians in Britain. Each religious and linguistic group is in turn differentiated along various castes and sects. The cultures of these groups and the sex/gender systems of which they are a part are correspondingly different.*
>
> (Brah, 1992, p. 64)

What, then, of the problems apparently faced by the young Asian women whom Dostiyo is seeking to help? Kalpana describes the needs of young women who do not wish to confirm to the 'traditional' roles mapped out for them, which may include an arranged marriage, and says that they suffer stress and depression due to 'the immense stress in terms of having to live in one culture at home and to live in another culture when they were at school'. The idea that younger members of minority communities in Britain experience a 'culture conflict' is a common one. 'Cultures are necessarily dynamic ... The culture (as a shared system of meaning) that young black adults now subscribe to has some roots in, but is not precisely that of their parents' (Westwood and Bhachu, 1988, p. 160).

Caught between two cultures – or is this view too simplistic?

However, Brah cautions against too easy an acceptance of the idea that traditional culture is somehow a 'problem' for young Asian women. Her own research paints a different picture, and at the same time shows how this accepted image of a 'clash of identity' can again play into stereotypical views, both of Asian women and of Asian culture generally:

> *There is a tendency among teachers to see most problems encountered by Asian girls as being the result of 'intergenerational conflict'. Yet there is no evidence to support the implied assertion that conflict levels are higher amongst Asian families than among white families. Asian parents tend to be portrayed as 'authoritarian', 'conservative' and supposedly 'opposed to the liberating influence of schools'. But there is as much variation among Asian parents on issues concerning the education of their children as can be expected in any other group of parents.*
>
> *[...]*
>
> *The great majority of the Asian adolescents [surveyed] expected their marriages to be arranged – a prospect they accepted because, unlike the media portrayal of bullying Asian parents ramming arranged marriages down the throats of their children, many adolescents felt confident that they would not be forced into a marriage that they did not want. It was evident that this confidence was not misplaced as most*

parents declared that they would not countenance forcing their children into a marriage against the latter's wishes. A significant majority of the parents saw the whole process as a joint undertaking between the parents and the young person.

(Brah, 1992, pp. 74, 72)

Shama Ahmed claims that there is sometimes a tendency among white professional workers to 'over-identify' with Asian young people, seeing them as 'westernized and therefore naturally "progressive"' (Ahmed, 1986, p. 147). Their use of clichés such as 'caught between two cultures' and 'held down by tradition-bound parents' may misrepresent the complexities of family and community circumstances. Such over-identification with Westernised young people, suggests Ahmed, can be attributed to a racism which sees the 'solution' in Asian communities assimilating Western values. However, she admits that such cases are not easy, even for workers from a similar cultural background.

Ahmed emphasises the importance of seeing cultural conflicts of this kind in a broader context:

> *Some Asian girls and young women, but by no means all, sometimes show a contempt for their parents, their colour and their culture. They may be ashamed to speak in their mother tongue or express a dislike of 'Pakis', including a refusal to see Asian social workers. Why these Asian youngsters show a strong preference for the dominant white majority group is frequently insufficiently understood by white practitioners. Clearly, these are deep problems of racial identity not just instances of adolescents making a bid for freedom. Yet this over-identification with white cultures is interpreted too readily by many practitioners as a positive indication of cultural assimilation. Such superficial interpretations can mean that interventions which require supporting positively a client's cultural and racial identity are rarely identified. Furthermore, this type of thinking and assessment suggests that 'Asianness' and 'West Indianness' are conditions to be overcome, and that salvation lies in adopting white culture; and any white culture is deemed superior to any black culture.*

> *(Ahmed, 1986, p. 149)*

This is yet another reminder of the danger of relying too much on cultural differences as an explanation for the experience of minority ethnic groups, and of the need to see such differences in the wider context of racism.

Key points

- Cultural differences can lead to tensions for some members of minority ethnic groups, particularly younger members who may feel 'caught' between two cultures.

- However, over-generalisations about 'cultural diversity' can result in prejudiced judgements and discriminatory responses.

- Cultural differences and conflicts need to be seen in the wider context of minority groups' experience, including the experience of racism.

Section 4
The challenge of racism

4.1 Racism and black families

In this section of the unit we will be looking more closely at the impact of racism on the lives of black and minority ethnic groups, and particularly at its impact on their needs for, and experience of, health and social care services. As Section 3 showed, popular images of black families often reflect limited knowledge and prejudiced attitudes towards minority ethnic communities. In the example of the extended family and the over-used cliché of 'culture conflict', you saw how such stereotypes overlook the complexities of life for people of Asian origin in Britain.

Negative stereotypes of African-Caribbean families are also widespread. The fourth section of the audio cassette for Block 3 contains extracts from an interview with Lynthia Grant, manager of Moyenda (Black Families Talking), a project based in west London which is part of Exploring Parenthood, a national charity. Although the project works with a wide range of black families, most of Moyenda's work is with families of African-Caribbean origin.

Black families: misrepresented by popular stereotypes

Activity 11   **Stereotypes of black people and black families**

Allow about 15 minutes   Listen to the fourth section of Audio Cassette 3 now (side 2). As you do
   so, make a note of the stereotypes of black people and black families
mentioned by Lynthia.

Comment   Lynthia says that the project sees its role as challenging the stereotyped
images of black families that exist, even among professionals. The
common image is one of 'a very dysfunctional family,' which includes the
idea that black families produce boys who end up as 'muggers' or in

prison. Later, she talks about how society sees black fathers in particular and black men in general: once again, the image is of them being 'no good' , 'irresponsible', and so on.

In the interview itself Lynthia challenges these common stereotypes – in her words 'to redress the balance in terms of how black families are seen'. For example, she says that, although there might be dysfunctional families within the black community, there are also plenty of black families that don't fit the stereotype. A survey carried out by Moyenda, of 241 black parents living mainly in Greater London and surrounding counties, questioned this popular image:

> *The survey findings challenged some widely held negative stereotypes of black families in British society, suggesting that attention should focus instead on black parents' need for more culturally appropriate, highly efficient and well resourced services to deal with the everyday problems of parenting ...*

> *The survey findings challenged the view that there are high rates of family breakdown and single parenting within the black communities. The researchers found well over half (60%) of parents were married and 6% were living with a partner. Only a third could be classified as 'lone parents', and they included 22% who were single, 8% who were separated, 2% who were widowed and just 1% who stated that they were divorced. They concluded that the majority of black children in this sample were being brought up in a two parent family home.*

> *The widely held view that large families are the norm amongst black people also did not hold true. Only 20% of parents were identified with four or more children. The overwhelming majority (55%) had no more than two children, of whom 22% had just one child.*

> *(Exploring Parenthood, 1995, p. 39)*

As with the examples of Asian families, evidence of this kind enables us to see popular stereotypes as generalisations which misrepresent the diversity of experience in minority ethnic groups. And just as Kalpana Desai placed the image of the Asian extended family in the context of social and family change, so Lynthia Grant sees the experience of African-Caribbean families against the backdrop of change between the generations and changes in society as a whole.

Changing attitudes and roles

There is a popular image of black parents as being very strict and disciplinarian with their children – as Lynthia says, 'not messing about with the belt'. Another generalisation, as you saw in the example of the Tyra Henry inquiry earlier, is that grandmothers play a key part in child rearing. Such stereotypes need to be seen in the context of changes and differences between generations in British black families. Lynthia talks about tensions over child rearing between black parents born and brought up in Britain and their own parents born in the Caribbean. Older people may assume that they will play a key role as grandparents, while their children may see this as 'interfering'. Those born in the Caribbean tend to be more disciplinarian with children, feeling 'it hasn't done them any harm and this society's just too free and easy'. This is confirmed by Moyenda's own research:

> *Work revealed variations in parenting attitudes and ideas amongst African-Caribbean parents and the concept of the African-Caribbean parent being 'strict and unbending' was challenged. Parents who were*

born here or came to the UK at an early age were very different in their thinking about parenting compared with parents who had spent a large part of their childhood in the Caribbean, where the concept of 'family' was perceived to be much broader than in Britain.

(*Exploring Parenthood*, 1995, p. 34)

These examples of generational change are evidence of the complexities which are overlooked in stereotypical generalisations about 'the black family'. They also reinforce the idea that emerged in the discussion of both the gypsy and Asian groups – that their culture cannot be isolated, is not static and is influenced by wider social change.

The changing context

Wider social and economic change may pose a challenge to dominant norms and values in minority ethnic groups. One such challenge is unemployment. It is not only black men who are suffering the effects of long-term, structural unemployment but they are suffering disproportionately. Mason quotes statistics that show that 18.3 per cent of minority ethnic adults were unemployed in 1991, compared with 8.8 per cent of white adults. Twenty-one per cent specifically of black (defined as Black-Caribbean, Black-African and Black-Other) adults, and around 25 per cent of black men, were out of work (Mason, 1995, p. 50). The black fathers' project set up by Moyenda is a positive response to the effects of unemployment, in particular the way it has undermined many black men's role as main economic provider for the family. The project is helping black men who find their breadwinner role disappearing to alter the way they see themselves and think about fatherhood more creatively.

Black men in Britain – a changing role?

As such changes take root, they will play a part in shifting norms and values right across society. This is a part of the complex process of cultural change. Neither the majority population in the UK nor minority ethnic groups live entirely 'inside' one culture, cut off from contact with other cultural groups. Increasingly, the lives of members of different communities overlap, and all of us are exposed to a variety of cultural experiences and influences. Television, advertising and 'consumer culture' make it impossible for even the most isolated minority group to avoid contact with society's 'mainstream' culture, or for the most narrow-minded member of the majority community to remain entirely unaware of the rich diversity of cultural life in modern Britain. Striking examples of this are occurring all the time in popular music and popular culture generally, such as the 'crossovers' between Jamaican reggae and traditional Asian 'bhangra' music, and the development of a street slang comprising English and Caribbean elements among both black and white young people in cities like London and Liverpool. In this kind of environment it is impossible to define either the culture of minority communities or 'mainstream' British culture as something fixed, with clear boundaries. As black sociologist Paul Gilroy says:

> *I think we need to be ... clear that no single culture is hermetically sealed off from others ... There can be no neat and tidy pluralistic separation of racial groups in this country ... Culture, even the culture which defines the groups we know as races, is never fixed, finished or final. It is fluid, it is actively and continually made and re-made.*

(Gilroy, 1992, p. 57)

Key points

- Racism may disadvantage black people, both in economic terms and through stereotyping by professionals.

- Minority group culture is not static but is heavily influenced by wider social and economic change.

4.2 The impact of racism

One of Moyenda's aims is to help black families to respond to and deal with the racism that they experience, and on the audio cassette Lynthia gives some examples of the impact of racism on families. Racism impacts on parenting, since black parents have to work hard to build up the self-esteem of a child who has already begun to absorb negative images of black people. Black parents have to make efforts to counter the negative messages about their ethnicity that black children absorb at school, and through books and the media. Stereotypical ideas about black men influence black men themselves, particularly in their role as fathers. Lynthia suggests: 'It doesn't make them very confident as fathers, because if you're constantly knocking at somebody that certainly is going to actually affect them ... I think what it does it actually has an effect on their self-esteem as black men.'

I noted in Section 3 that racism can influence how black people experience service provision and delivery. In social work Lena Dominelli claims that racism 'operates through two channels which shape client–worker interactions: the exclusive channel and the inclusive one.' The *exclusive* channel results 'in black people having limited access to the "goodies" or caring services provided through social work intervention'; while the *inclusive* channel has produced a situation, Dominelli claims, in which black people are over-represented in services which 'are more directly engaged in controlling people's behaviour' (Dominelli, 1992, pp. 165–6).

Activity 12   Experiencing the 'two channels'

Allow about 10 minutes   (a)   Note down any examples you can recall from earlier in this unit of the exclusive channel in health and social care services – in other words, of members of minority ethnic groups being denied access to services they need.

(b)   Use Section 2.2 and any experience you have to suggest those areas of social work practice where black people and other minority ethnic groups might be over-represented.

Comment   (a)   In the *exclusive* channel you might have noted the Asian elders' lack of access to meals on wheels. (Dominelli notes that black elders are also under-represented among people receiving home helps and sheltered accommodation). In health services, you may have suggested GPs' reluctance to visit traveller sites.

(b)   On the *inclusive* side, you may have noted Karen McHugh's comment that social workers see gypsy children as inherently 'at risk' and often place them on the child protection register needlessly. This might suggest to you that minority groups are more likely to be labelled and policed by professionals. Black people are over-represented in areas where social workers have a policing role, such as putting children into care and assisting in admissions to psychiatric hospitals.

People of African-Caribbean origin are more likely than white people to be diagnosed as schizophrenic and 'a diagnosis of schizophrenia is around five times more likely for African-Caribbean males ... when compared with their white counterparts' (Mason, 1995, p. 99). Some studies suggest that the tendency to diagnose black patients as schizophrenic may be a result of the racism of Western-trained medical staff (Fernando, 1991). However, other studies have claimed that the diagnosis of schizophrenia may in fact be accurate, and that the greater incidence of this and other mental illnesses among black people may be a direct result of their experience of racism:

> *These seem to be real cases of schizophrenia ... It's not just a question of poverty. It is a question of racism. A large proportion of people in any society are vulnerable to mental illness but many of them live with stresses without becoming ill. My strong feeling is that black people are being driven psychotic by our society, that racism is indeed causing these high rates of mental illness.*
>
> (Berry and O'Dwyer, 1987, p. 13)

Social workers make disproportionate use of referral into care for minority ethnic children. Research in one London borough in the mid-1980s found that black children constituted 52 per cent of the borough's children in care although they formed only 40 per cent of the child population (Barn, cited in Skellington, 1996). Over half of these children

Likely to get a fair deal from welfare services? Black young people at the Notting Hill Carnival

were of African-Caribbean origin. Barn claimed that black children were admitted into care 'from situations where preventive strategies could have been attempted' and found that black children entered care more quickly than white children:

> Barn's study ... demonstrated the important role racial stereotypes play in pathologizing black families ... Barn explained differences in the referral and admission patterns of black and white children in terms of social workers' perceptions of individual cases set against the context of the disadvantaged position of black families in the areas of housing and employment and the greater likelihood of such families needing social services help.
>
> (Skellington, 1996, p. 128)

Social and economic disadvantage, it appears, combines with negative attitudes towards black families to bring about a situation in which black people's experience of welfare services is significantly different from, and less favourable than, that of their white counterparts.

Key points

- The experience of racism can lead to specific health and social care needs for black people.

- Black people's exclusion from the supportive aspects of health and social care services is paralleled by their over-representation in services with a 'controlling' aspect.

Section 5
Working towards equality

This final main section of the unit looks at some of the ways in which health and social care agencies can respond to the challenge of racism. In particular, it focuses on new ideas emerging from projects in which minority ethnic groups themselves have participated. Such initiatives suggest that a diversity of types of service – voluntary as well as statutory – will be needed in order to respond to the diverse needs of the UK population as a whole. It must be acknowledged that this risks putting the onus on minorities to 'provide for their own' and may allow mainstream statutory services to continue unchanged. In fact, statutory services need to incorporate new insights and demonstrate their own practical commitment to non-discriminatory service provision.

5.1 Minority initiatives

The Moyenda project – a grassroots initiative

We start by reviewing the work of the Moyenda project which you first encountered in Section 4. Moyenda sees its aim as challenging racist attitudes towards black families and supporting them in dealing with the impact of racism in their lives. The project is funded by charitable donations and local authority grants but is firmly embedded in the black community which it serves.

Activity 13 **Working with black families**

Allow about 10 minutes

Make a note of what you see as the main features of Moyenda's approach to working with black families, as Lynthia Grant explains them. If you need to, listen again to this section of the audio cassette.

Comment I noticed the following five features in Moyenda's approach.

1   It builds on the black community's existing resources and networks and taps into these. Lynthia describes the work that the project has done with churches and other religious groups in the locality.

2   Although it was a new project it did not set up something new – whereas some organisations working with black people set up a 'brand new support group', which may cause resentment.

3   It builds on the community's strengths – Lynthia talks about acknowledging black people's 'spirituality', and their development of 'coping strategies' to deal with racism.

4   It responds to expressed needs from black people themselves rather than setting a new agenda.

5   It involves people who are part of, or can identify with, the group that the project aims to help and who have a real understanding of their culture and experiences.

Many of these features can be found in other thriving projects, such as those discussed in Unit 11 and in Section 3 of this unit. You might have noted that Kalpana Desai describes in similar terms how Dostiyo's work builds on existing contacts and networks within Asian groups in

Northampton. Both Dostiyo and Moyenda are managed and staffed by members of the minority ethnic groups with which the projects are working. Many of the 15,000 community health projects in the UK, sometimes supported by statutory funding but operating at grass roots level, display similar qualities of flexibility and responsiveness.

The fifth feature listed in the comment may be difficult to achieve if projects are not 'homegrown'. Workers at Dostiyo and Moyenda are unlikely to misunderstand or misinterpret aspects of the culture of the communities they work with in the way that members of 'outside' agencies might do. They have a shared experience of prejudice and discrimination, which not only gives them an understanding of people's needs but also helps to build up a sense of trust. An 'outsider' might find this more difficult to establish, particularly if community members had negative experiences of external agencies.

This is not to say that grassroots agencies necessarily have an easy time. You'll remember Kalpana talking about the suspicion and hostility from some Asian men about aspects of Dostiyo's work with women, particularly their work in the area of sexual health. On the other hand, it is difficult to imagine an external agency staffed completely by white workers making any headway in the community with a sensitive issue of this kind.

Grassroots initiatives can build on the spiritual resources of minority groups

Jewish welfare initiatives – a study in separatism?

Dostiyo and Moyenda are fairly recent initiatives, and older minority ethnic groups in Britain often have more established networks of welfare provision. A good example of this is the Jewish community. It has been an important presence in the UK for hundreds of years, although its members have often experienced prejudice and hostility from the majority population.

In 1996, the Manchester Jewish Museum organised an exhibition with the title 'Taking care of ourselves', which aimed to reflect the range of welfare organisations in the Jewish community in Britain. The final section of the audio cassette for Block 3 consists of a conversation between Adrienne Walman, director of the museum, and Magda Segal, a freelance photographer employed to take pictures for the exhibition of Jewish welfare organisations in Manchester. They explore arguments for separate services targeted at Jewish people.

Activity 14   ### Welfare services in the Jewish community

Allow about 10 minutes

Listen to this final section of Audio Cassette 3 now. Make notes of the arguments put forward for having specific organisations for Jewish people, provided by Jewish people themselves.

Comment   While she acknowledges the important role played by what she calls 'general provision', Adrienne Walman argues that the Jewish community has particular cultural, social and religious needs, which Jewish-run organisations are best placed to meet. In a sense, what Adrienne describes here is a response to the kind of situation that we looked at earlier in the unit, where members of minority groups feel excluded from services because the provision is not geared to their cultural needs.

Adrienne's argument is that a service provided specially for Jewish people, by a Jewish organisation aware of the community's customs and attitudes, is able to meet cultural needs in a way that a mainstream service never could. She gives the example of a home for older Jewish people which has a synagogue, where Jewish festivals are celebrated and where residents are able to live alongside members of their own community, whom they may have known since childhood.

A minority group of long-standing in Britain: Hasidic Jews in North London

You'll note that Jewish people are also engaging with 'new issues and new groups' – Jewish Women's Aid, the Jewish AIDS Trust, and a controversial initiative to tackle drug taking among Jewish young people are mentioned. As with the work of Dostiyo and Moyenda on sensitive issues, it could be argued that, despite community resistance, an 'insider' organisation will be more successful in this than a mainstream or external agency. This in turn raises the question of whether separate services should be provided for (and perhaps by) members of minority ethnic groups.

Residential and foster care – integration or separation?

Let's look now at an area where the battle over separate services has been raging – the field of childcare. You have already come across an argument for separate residential care for black children and older people in Unit 8. The work you having been doing in this unit should also help you to think through these debates – and to weigh up the evidence for and against separate services.

Activity 15 **Arguments for and against separate residential care**

Allow about 20 minutes

Review the discussion in Section 3.4 of Unit 8 and in this unit, and re-read Chapter 11 in the Reader, 'Black perspectives on residential care'. Then write down at least one argument *for* and one *against* separate residential care for black children.

Comment

Among the arguments for separate services you might have noted the following.

1   Mainstream residential care has failed black people because it has been not only unequal and inappropriate, but inaccessible and unavailable as well.

2   Members of the black community who have received mainstream residential care have experienced prejudice and racism which has undermined their dignity and black identity.

3   Stereotypes of black families 'looking after their own' have served to deny services to people in need of residential care.

4   Black-led voluntary and private organisations are best placed to understand racism and cultural traditions, to maintain links with the wider black community and to provide appropriate care by black adults.

Among the arguments you might have developed against separate services could be the following.

1   Encouraging separate services might let statutory services 'off the hook' of dealing with prejudice and discrimination.

2   No minority ethnic group is entirely separate and each is dynamic in response to external change. Provision of separate services could lead to an over-emphasis on difference while common issues and problems like poverty are ignored.

3   Care by white people is better than a lack of any service at all.

4   If minority groups stay 'in the system' they can fight for better services for all.

One of the most controversial aspects of the debate about black children in care has been the practice of 'trans-racial' fostering and adoption. John Small, one of the key campaigners against trans-racial adoption, has argued that placing black children with white families leads to children developing a confused sense of their own identity:

> *Many transracially adopted children are aware that the lighter their skin colour the more desirable they are to white society, and many feel it is better to be white than black ... The denial of the reality of the visibility of the black child in a white family creates the pre-condition for the phenomenon of identity confusion. Many, although black, will grow up believing or wishing that they were white.*
>
> *(Small, 1986, p. 82)*

To ignore ethnic origin in placing children with families, Small claims, is to overlook the reality of prejudice and discrimination: 'To tell the child that colour in this society does not matter is to ignore the racism in the society'. In common with other critics of trans-racial placements, Small sees them as reflecting the erroneous assumption, based on negative stereotypes, that there are no suitable black families that could foster or adopt black children. According to this view, placing black children with black families or in black-run homes would help to create a positive black identity.

The argument that 'white-run' child care, whether with foster parents or in a residential home, is damaging to black children, is reflected in this poem by Margaret Parr:

It's bad for your child to be in care

I can't face this life alone
'cos I've always lived in a home
Thrown out at seventeen
with no friends or family
Thank-you social services
for your hospitality.
Here I am in a black community
I've grown up 'white' but they can't see
Which do I turn to – white or black?
I daren't step forward, I can't step back
Help me someone please
To find my culture and identity
Why could I not have these when I was young?
They brought me up to think being black is wrong.
Black people out there
You've got to be aware
For it's bad for your child to be in care.

(University of Essex, Children's Legal Centre, 1984, in Gambe *et al.*, 1992)

On the other hand, there have been criticisms of this view, including some from within the black community. Black sociologist Paul Gilroy has argued against detaching 'black identity' from other kinds of identity and attachment, for example those shaped by 'age, gender, class or neighbourhood considerations' (Gilroy, 1987, p. 65). It may well be that racist views about black families lead to many black children being taken into care and to black parents not being seen as 'suitable' adopters. But we must not be blinkered about 'same race' adoption. Its advocates tend to see ethnicity as the only factor in a child's identity. They see the black community as a separate entity within the wider society, rather than as overlapping and interacting with it. Gilroy claims that this approach is 'sadly misplaced in this country where the black population is too small, too diverse and too fragmented to be conceptualised as a single cohesive nation' (1987, p. 66).

Key points

* 'Outsider' and statutory health and social care agencies can learn from grassroots initiatives which are sensitive and responsive to the culture and experiences of groups with which they work.

* The debate about separate services for minority ethnic groups is important, but should not distract statutory agencies from tackling prejudice and discrimination themselves.

5.2 Changing mainstream services

Letting statutory agencies off the hook?

In the final audio extract which you listened to for Activity 14, Magda Segal describes two examples of welfare services in the Jewish community in Manchester: the soup kitchen, which distributes food to people living on their own, and the organisation which offers practical help and support to new mothers. This rounds off the picture of a community caring for itself, rather than relying on outside agencies. Magda's own response to these initiatives is clearly a positive one. As she says: 'I suppose what I was left with feeling when I'd finished the project is that, when you're old, the place to be is Manchester and the thing to be is Jewish, because everybody seems to be – it is a community and people seem to be cared for.'

If this is the case, where does this leave statutory agencies? One of the dangers of arguing for self-help or community-run initiatives, is that mainstream services and the majority population can absolve themselves of responsibility. As you saw earlier in the unit, service providers can argue that minority groups are best able to look after themselves – in their extended families, close-knit communities and voluntary groups. This can become a way of avoiding responsibility for challenging racism in mainstream practice, and for ensuring that services are equally available to all. Many voluntary groups, however, see putting pressure on mainstream services as a key part of their role. Both Kalpana Desai and Lynthia Grant make it clear that an important part of their projects' work is challenging racism in mainstream services and changing the way these services work.

Working for change

This is a good point to review what mainstream providers (or anyone providing a service) might do to ensure that their services are accessible and appropriate to the needs of all groups. I shall use the case of the mother and toddler group, taken from Kalpana Desai's comments on

Working for change in mainstream services: the Dostiyo project for Asian women and girls, Northampton

the third section of the audio cassette. Many of the Bangladeshi women, you'll recall, have young children and are at home by themselves for most of the day. They do not attend the existing mother and toddler group in the area, even though the group is keen to attract them.

Kalpana suggests that the Bangladeshi women don't see the group as accessible and feel that no one there understands them. Few of the Bangladeshi women speak English, but there are probably other issues here besides language. Dostiyo has set up a separate group, specifically for the Bangladeshi women and their children, but hopes at some point to integrate the Bangladeshi group with the mainstream group. How is this to be achieved?

Activity 16   Towards integration

Allow about 10 minutes   Review the knowledge and understanding you have gained by working through this unit. Then use it to formulate at least two ideas which might assist the organiser of the mainstream mother and toddler group in achieving a merger between the groups.

Comment   Here are a few ideas drawn from this unit.

1   Improve access for members of the Bangladeshi group. This might include reviewing opening hours, checking that the venue is appropriate, and changing publicity.

2   Become more sensitive and responsive to minority needs, for example by reviewing activities so that they reflect minority experience and culture. This might include acquiring more diverse books and toys, changing poster displays.

3   Challenge racism. Have a clear policy on racial harassment.

4   Take a positive approach to diversity. Ensure that the helpers are people from varied backgrounds, including Bangladeshi women if possible.

Below are some ideas from a project that I worked with, which set out to change its practice so that it became more accessible to members of local minority ethnic groups. The project was set up by a national charity to provide education and training to unemployed people in a multi-ethnic inner London borough. Recognising its failure to attract significant numbers of users from black and minority ethnic groups in the area, the project embarked on a long-term process of change which involved the following steps:

• changing the management structure of the project to reflect groups from across the local community

• changing the composition of the staff group to reflect the diversity of the community

• building up strong links with groups and networks in the minority communities

• ensuring that the project's activities reflected the cultural needs and interests of local communities

• overhauling all publicity and other materials to ensure that they included positive images of members of minority communities

• adopting and monitoring a policy on racial harassment and the use of language within the project.

A number of points are worth emphasising here. First, and most important, is that mainstream welfare agencies themselves have to change if they are to meet the needs of minority ethnic groups. Often agencies have implicitly adopted an 'assimilationist' view, believing that members of minority groups simply need to adapt and assimilate to the 'mainstream' culture. Such assumptions 'tended to place the onus for change and adaptation squarely on the shoulders of the excluded and, hence, to blame the victims of inequality for their own situations' (Mason, 1995, p. 2). The aim of assimilationist initiatives 'is to change the people to match existing services, rather than altering services to meet people's perceived needs' (Donovan, 1986, p. 45). One report on social services departments' services for minority ethnic communities comments that:

> the assimilationist perspective suggests that the services provided by SSDs [social services departments] are, basically, sound and do not require modification or change. SSDs are in the business of responding to those in 'need' and if members of the black and minority ethnic community fall into one of these categories then they can take advantage of the services provided. If there is any dysfunction between services provided and the needs of the black and minority ethnic communities, the onus is on the community to change and accommodate existing practice.
>
> (Butt et al., 1994, p. 5)

A second point is that adapting an organisation to meet the diversity of needs within the local community means change at every level – from the images used in publicity material (as Lynthia Grant at Moyenda realised) through to the representation of black and minority ethnic people in the staffing and management of the organisation.

Finally, although all of these measures can be seen as implicitly challenging prejudice and discrimination, there need to be specific policies – such as the policies on racist language and racial harassment mentioned earlier – aimed at outlawing racism within the organisation, and training and support for staff in understanding and implementing them.

Challenging racism in mainstream services

Some of the discussion in this unit has been critical of health and social care services for minority ethnic groups, and the unit has focused on the shortcomings of some statutory agencies in responding to diversity within the community. However, it is important to recognise the steps that many agencies are taking to challenge racism and provide more equal services. Over the past two decades a wide variety of initiatives have been attempted. Examples are steps to recruit and promote staff from minority ethnic groups and training programmes which challenge racism and promote equality of opportunity both in the workplace and in service provision.

Many organisations have also produced guidelines for anti-racist or anti-discriminatory practice in the particular field in which they are working. The Central Council for Education and Training in Social Work (CCETSW) has been active in this area, although its work has been controversial – attracting some strong support, but being seen in some quarters as foisting 'politically correct doctrines' on social workers (Pinker, 1993). CCETSW has produced a wide range of publications in the field of equal opportunities and anti-racism, covering all the main

Working for cultural diversity: preparing food for lunch for Asian elders at a day centre

areas of social work practice. Responding to the kinds of concern about black children in care outlined in Section 5.1, a CCETSW publication aimed at improving practice in childcare produced the guidelines below for social work staff.

Meeting the needs of black children in care: an agenda for change

If taking over the care of the child by the local authority is the only way that the needs of the child can be met, then:

1   it is appropriate for the local authority to plan for black children

2   local authorities should initially divert resources towards the establishment of a network of family contacts to support the black family in difficulties. If it is necessary for the local authority to provide care for a black child, this should be with a substitute black family. If family placement is not appropriate, residential care must take into account a child's racial, religious, linguistic and cultural needs and all care must include plans to maintain contact with the child's own family and community.

Child care should ensure that the child's developmental needs are provided for. By development, we mean:

(a)   Food: for a black child the carer should be sensitive and avoid giving the child food which he or she should not eat either because of their religion or tradition.

(b)   Clothing: the child should be provided with and encouraged to have a positive and appreciative view of the clothes of his or her cultural background.

(c)   Cosmetics: an understanding and appreciation of the special place cosmetics have in the life of a black child is very important; for example, black children need particular hair and skin creams.

(d)   Accommodation/home: the child needs an environment which reflects and positively reinforces his or her personal, social and cultural identity.

(e)   Emotional development: for children to have a well-adjusted personality, they need to feel secure and develop positive self-images. Children need love and affection in order to feel secure. In a racist society, black groups are always subject to criticism and ridicule. Black children need to be placed with black carers who are and can provide positive role models.

Social workers and carers should be aware that racism damages all children, white and black. It disadvantages white children by giving them a false sense of superiority and a distorted picture of the world they live in. It undervalues and damages black children and gives them a distorted view of themselves and that of society.

(f)   Social development and positive identity: black children need to have contact with and feel part of the black community in the widest sense. Black children need to be able to carry their past into the present and be sustained into the future. A key element of this must include a positive sense of their culture in their history or roots.

(g)   Education: a black child needs to develop the fundamental attributes of speech, thought, self-consciousness and identity to become a competent member of his or her community. This sense of education is on the whole deficient in formal educational institutions. Carers should take a keen interest in seeing that the content of the formal schooling that the child receives is not racist. Black children's self-confidence and identity depend upon their language forms and accents being valued and given credibility e.g. mother tongue, Patois and Creole.

(h)   Health: a black child requires his or her health needs to be met and maintained. Formal care tends to ignore the specific needs of black children, e.g. sickle cell anaemia.

(Gambe et al., 1992, pp. 59–60)

Within the health sector, guidelines and recommendations have been developed for staff working with multi-ethnic groups. The box below is an example of guidelines developed for health visitors.

Guidelines for health visitors

The clinic should be a welcoming environment that values different races. Health visitors should ensure that toys, books, posters, leaflets, signs and health education material available in the clinic reflect the multi-racial society that Britain has become. Dolls that are both black and white are essential. Books should reflect positive images of black children and adults, and should be relevant to different cultures. Signs and clinic times should be in suitable languages. A notice saying welcome in a number of languages would give the impression that staff are aware that not everyone speaks English as a first language. Similarly celebrating different religious festivals in addition to Christmas and Easter would enable people to feel their religions are acknowledged and valued. However, it is obviously important to identify which religious occasions clients using the clinic would normally celebrate.

(Health Visitors' Association, 1989, pp. 38–9)

These recommendations acknowledge, although in very different ways, that health and social care services need to examine closely every aspect of their own practice, and be prepared to meet the challenge of radical change, if they are serious about meeting the needs of a population that is increasingly diverse, and where there are deep-rooted inequalities.

Activity 17 What needs to change?

Allow about 30 minutes

As a final activity, I would like you to think of a health or care service that you know well. It may be one that you work in or have worked in, or one that you are familiar with as a service user. If you are stuck for an example, you could choose your local GP or dental surgery, or hospital accident and emergency department, or an advice service such as the Citizens Advice Bureau. Think for a few minutes about whether the service is meeting the diversity of needs within the local community it serves. Make brief notes in answer to these questions.

(a) What are the main ethnic groups in the local community covered by the service?

(b) How accessible is the service to these groups at present? (Think about issues such as location, languages and images used, timing of services, sensitivity to cultural needs.)

(c) What kinds of change might need to take place to ensure that the service was equally accessible and relevant to all groups in the community? (You may want to look back over the examples in this section to help you.)

Comment

There are many different ways you could have answered these questions, depending on the kind of service you chose and the range of needs in the local community. Whatever your answer, I hope that doing this activity enabled you to examine more closely the relationship between health and social care services and the diversity of groups they aim to serve. I hope you saw that there are practical changes that agencies can make, in order to provide a service that is equally accessible and appropriate to the needs of all in the community.

Key points

- The work of community or self-help groups does not absolve statutory agencies of the responsibility to challenge racism and respond to the diversity of needs in local communities.

- Minority ethnic organisations have an important role in challenging prejudice and encouraging change in statutory or mainstream services.

- Mainstream health and social care agencies have a responsibility to challenge racism in their own organisations and to work to ensure that services reflect the diversity of the population they serve.

- Challenging racism and improving practice is the responsibility of everyone with a concern for health and social care.

Conclusion

Your work on this unit should have left you with some idea of the variety of traditions and values to be found in modern British society, and some sense of how this cultural diversity affects people's experience of health and social care provision. The detailed study of the experience of four minority groups has revealed the limitations of making simple links between a group's culture and the ways in which members of the group experience health and social care services. As you have seen, while a group's traditions and values may have some influence on attitudes to health and social care, the attitudes that members of minority groups encounter from care workers and services are of much greater importance. *Stereotypes*, based on limited and often misleading information, can reinforce *prejudice* and lead to actions which *discriminate* against minority ethnic groups and deny them access to the services they need. At the same time, *racism* leads to wider, structural inequalities – for example, in employment and housing – which themselves create needs for care and support. Although many of the accounts you have heard paint a gloomy picture of the experiences of black and minority ethnic groups, you have also seen examples of what can be done, and is being done, to challenge racism and to make sure that health and social care services are equally available and appropriate for all in the community. The positive challenges offered by grassroots initiatives within minority communities, of the kind this unit has examined, offer a powerful signal to statutory agencies to look critically at their own practice and take practical steps to bring about change.

You have reached the end of your work on the main units in Block 3 of the course. You should now have a clearer understanding of the range of health and social care services provided to local communities, and of some of the key issues involved in ensuring that services meet the needs of diverse and changing communities. Your work in Unit 13 will give you a chance to put what you have learned about community-based services into practice, and to develop your skills in matching services to a range of individual needs. Throughout Block 3, and particularly in Unit 12, we have emphasised the importance of valuing and building on the experiences of service users, especially those whose voices have been marginalised by prejudice and discrimination. In Block 4 we will be looking in more detail at ways of placing people's life experience at the heart of caring relationships.

Study skills: Choosing a course for next year

You have just received literature from the OU (or are about to receive it) on choosing a course to follow K100. Are you ready to think so far ahead when you are not yet half-way through K100? Well, you have a few weeks before you need to return the form and you can change your mind for some time after that (the relevant dates are given in the literature) – but here are some first thoughts.

If you decide to take another OU course you can, in principle, choose virtually any on offer – from *Astronomy and Planetary Science* to *Homer: Poetry and Society*. However, if you are looking to build on what you are learning in K100, the obvious choices are the Level 2 courses in the School of Health and Social Welfare. Actually, you are free to go straight to a third-level course, but perhaps you should think about your marks for your K100 assignments and ask your tutor's advice before deciding to skip a level. Alternatively, you might prefer to stay at Level 1 for another year and take, say, the Social Sciences Faculty's Level 1 course. (At one time all OU students took two Level 1 courses.)

If you *are* choosing an SHSW Level 2 course, you should look at how the Diploma in Health and Social Welfare works. Or you might want to explore details of the Diploma in Social Work/ Higher Education. Beyond SHSW, there are relevant courses in the Faculties of Social Sciences and Science, the Open University Business School and in the School of Education. Alternatively, you might prefer to concentrate on vocational training, or to transfer your OU credits and study in another university.

With so much choice, you may feel in need of advice. OU Regional Centres generally try to arrange 'course choice' events at a range of convenient locations during this period. You can also ask your tutor, either at a tutorial or over the phone. And, as always, talking to fellow students may be the most helpful avenue of all.

References

Ahmed, S. (1986) 'Cultural racism in work with Asian women and girls' in Ahmed, Cheetham and Small (1986).

Ahmed, S., Cheetham, J. and Small, J. (1986) *Social Work with Black Children and their Families*, Batsford/British Agencies for Adoption and Fostering, London.

Benzeval, M., Judge, K. and Whitehead, M. (1995) 'Introduction' in Benzeval, M., Judge, K. and Whitehead, M. (eds) *Tackling Inequalities in Health: An Agenda for Action*, King's Fund, London.

Berry, D. and O'Dwyer, N. (1987) 'Is racism driving blacks out of their minds?', *Guardian*, 30 September, p. 13.

Bhalla, A. and Blakemore, K. (1981) *Elders of the Minority Ethnic Groups*, AFFOR (All Faiths for One Race), Birmingham.

Bhanu, B.R. (1996) 'Community care: the experiences of two South Asian communities in relation to caring for older people', a thesis submitted for the degree of Doctor of Philosophy, University of Durham (unpublished).

Brah, A. (1992) 'Women of South Asian origin in Britain: issues and concerns' in Braham, Rattansi and Skellington (1992).

Braham, P., Rattansi, A. and Skellington, R. (eds) (1992) *Racism and Antiracism: Inequalities, Opportunities and Policies*, Sage, London.

Butt, J., Garbach, P. and Ahmed, B. (1994) *Equally Fair? A Report on Social Services Departments' Development, Implementation and Monitoring of Services for the Black and Minority Ethnic Community*, HMSO, London.

Cameron, E., Evers, H. and Badger, F. (1989) 'Black older women, disability and health carers' in Jefferys, M. (ed.) *Growing Old in the Twentieth Century*, Routledge, London.

Department of Health (1995) *Variations in Health, What can the Department of Health and the NHS Do? Report of the Variations Sub-group of the Chief Medical Officer's Health of the Nation Working Group*, HMSO, London.

Dominelli, L. (1992) 'An uncaring profession? An examination of racism in social work' in Braham, Rattansi and Skellington (1992).

Donovan, J. (1986) *We Don't Buy Sickness, It Just Comes: Health, Illness and Health Care in the Lives of Black People in London*, Gower, Aldershot.

Exploring Parenthood (1995) *Moyenda Project Report 1991–1994*, Exploring Parenthood, London.

Fernando, S. (1991) *Mental Health, Race and Culture*, Macmillan/MIND, London.

Fryer, P. (1984) *Staying Power: The History of Black People in Britain*, Pluto Press, London.

Gambe, D., Gomes, J., Kapur, V., Rangel, M. and Stubbs, P. (1992) *Improving Practice with Children and Families: A Training Manual*, Central Council for Education and Training in Social Work, London.

Gilroy, P. (1987) *There Ain't No Black in the Union Jack: The Cultural Politics of Race and Nation*, Hutchinson, London.

Gilroy, P. (1992) 'The end of antiracism' in Donald, J. and Rattansi, A. (1992) *'Race', Culture and Difference*, Sage, London.

Gunaratnam, Y. (1993) 'Breaking the silence: Asian carers in Britain' in Bornat, J., Pereira, C., Pilgrim, D. and Williams, F. (eds) (1993) *Community Care: A Reader,* Macmillan/The Open University, London.

Health Visitors' Association (1989) *Entitled to be Healthy: Health Visiting and School Nursing in a Multi-racial Society,* HVA, London.

Jones, L.J. (1994) *The Social Context of Health and Health Work,* Macmillan, London.

Layton-Henry, Z. (1984) *The Politics of Race in Britain,* Allen & Unwin, London.

London Borough of Lambeth (1987) *Whose Child? The Report of the Panel Appointed to Look into the Death of Tyra Henry,* Borough of Lambeth, London.

Mason, D. (1995) *Race and Ethnicity in Modern Britain,* Oxford University Press, Oxford.

Patel, N.A. (1990) *'Race' Against Time: Social Services Provision to Black Elders,* Runnymede Trust, London.

Pinker, R. (1993) 'A lethal kind of looniness', *The Times Higher,* 10 September.

Shah, R. (1992) *The Silent Minority: Children with Disabilities in Asian Families,* National Children's Bureau, London.

Skellington, R. (1996) *'Race' in Britain Today,* Sage/The Open University, London.

Smaje, C. (1995) *Health, 'Race' and Ethnicity: Making Sense of the Evidence,* King's Fund, London.

Small, J. (1986) 'Transracial placements: conflicts and contradictions' in Ahmed, Cheetham, and Small (1986).

University of Essex, Children's Legal Centre (1984) *Black and In Care Conference Report,* Blackrose Press, London.

Westwood, S. and Bhachu, P. (eds) (1988) *Enterprising Women: Ethnicity, Economy and Gender Relations,* Routledge, London.

Young, M. and Willmott, P. (1962) (first published 1957) *Family and Kinship in East London,* Pelican Books, London.

Acknowledgements

Grateful acknowledgement is made to the following sources for permission to reproduce material in this unit:

Text

pp. 133 and 154–5: Gambe, D. *et al.* (1992) *Improving Practice with Children and Families: A Training Manual*, pp. 108–9 and 59–60, CCETSW; *p. 150*: Parr, M. (1984) 'It's bad for your child to be in care' in Gambe, D. *et al.* (1992) *Improving Practice with Children and Families: A Training Manual*, CCETSW, courtesy of Children's Legal Centre, University of Essex.

Illustrations

pp. 116, 147 (right): Crispin Hughes/Photofusion; *pp. 118 (left), 136*: Caroline Mardon/Photofusion; *pp. 118 (right), 125*: Gary Simpson/ Photofusion; *pp. 121, 138*: C. Stadtler/Photofusion; *pp. 130, 142, 156*: David Montford/Photofusion; *p. 132 (left)*: Steve Eason/Photofusion; *p. 132 (right)*: David Gibson/Photofusion; *p. 140*: Bob Watkins/ Photofusion; *p. 145*: Peter Marshall/Photofusion; *p. 147 (left)*: Robin McCartney/Photofusion; *p. 148*: J. Southworth/Photofusion; *p. 151*: Paul Bingham.

Unit 13
Finding Out about Services in the Community

Prepared for the course team by Martin Robb

While you are working on Unit 13, you will need:
- *The Good Study Guide*
- Skills video
- Care in the UK

Contents

Introduction

Unit 13 focuses on:
- assessing individual needs
- finding out about services in the community
- enabling people to make use of services
- reviewing progress on study skills
- tackling examinations
- working with numbers.

In Block 3 we have been exploring the relationship between health and care services and the communities that they serve. In this unit the focus is on developing your own skills in working in the community. It may be that you have a lot of experience of working in community settings, either as a paid worker or as a volunteer. Perhaps the kind of community-based health and care services described in Units 10–12 were familiar to you from your own experience. If this is the case, this unit will give you an opportunity to reflect on some of the skills that you have gained through this work and to gather evidence of them. Or it may be that you are involved in care work, but not in a community setting. If so, this unit may help you develop skills that will be useful in the future. Finally, you may not be directly involved in any form of care work, whether paid or unpaid. However, I hope that working through the activities in this unit will help to consolidate what you have learnt in Units 10–12, by giving you the chance to apply it to some practical examples.

Central themes of the unit

The particular skill that this unit focuses on is *finding out about services in the community*. In Unit 10 you encountered some of the difficulties in gaining access to services provided in the community. Part of the problem lies in finding out *what* services are available and *who* provides them. In Unit 12 we saw how lack of appropriate information can deny access to services for members of minority ethnic groups. We also explored some of the issues involved in matching health and care services to the diverse needs to be found in local communities.

The aim of this unit is to help you develop skills in gathering information about services in the local community, and in matching services to a range of individual needs. As far as the principles of good practice go, the unit is particularly relevant to promoting and supporting people's rights to appropriate services.

This unit presents a series of linked activities. The activities make use of a number of short case studies which feature individuals with a range of needs. I want you to imagine that the individuals featured in the case studies live in *your own local area* and to find out about local services which meet their needs. I have tried to ensure that you will be able to carry out all the activities from your own home or study base. However, if you find you have difficulties carrying out some of the activities, please talk to your tutor about what to do.

Unit 13 video content

Scene 7 'Finding out about services' follows two fictional characters, Mandy Brown and her two-year-old son Sean, as they search for information about services provided in their local community.

Section 1
Assessing needs

To make the process of finding out about services and facilities as real as possible, I have chosen to concentrate on a few individual cases. The first few activities will introduce you to them, and involve you in making a brief assessment of the needs of the individuals featured.

Activity 1   Assessing individual needs

Allow about 30 minutes

There are three case studies below. They are fictitious but drawn from real life. I have tried to illustrate the range of needs and contexts which community-based workers may find themselves dealing with. Read through the examples now.

Case study 1

Mandy Brown is a 19-year-old white woman. She is a lone parent, living in a rented flat with a two-year-old son, Sean. She moved to the area quite recently with her partner Gary, who has since left her, and she doesn't know anyone locally. Mandy needs money to support herself and Sean. She has an interview for a part-time job at a factory a few miles away, but there is no workplace crèche and she doesn't know where she could leave Sean. She doesn't have a car and has to rely on buses and taxis. Mandy thinks she may be entitled to more welfare benefits than she's getting. An additional worry is that the flat is damp and Sean has bad asthma.

Case study 2

Mohammed and Zeinab Bhatti are in their seventies and live in their own house. Mr Bhatti ran a small business until forced to retire after a bad fall a few years ago. He is increasingly frail and dependent on his wife to help him around the house and to carry out household chores. However, Mrs Bhatti has arthritis and is beginning to find the role of full-time carer a difficult one. The Bhattis are Muslim; they came to Britain from Pakistan 20 years ago. They have two grown-up children – their son is working in Pakistan and their daughter has moved with her husband to another town and is unable to help on a regular basis. Mr Bhatti feels cut off from social contacts – he used to be active in the local Asian community and had a wide circle of friends. Mrs Bhatti would like some help looking after her husband and to have an occasional break from household chores.

> ### Case study 3
>
> Colin Grant is a 35-year-old African-Caribbean man, born and brought up in Britain. He has learning difficulties and lives at home with his parents. Mr Grant senior works as an electrician for the local council, while Mrs Grant has not had a job since Colin was born. When he was younger, Colin attended a special school and a number of day centres, but a change in Mr Grant senior's job has meant a house move to a new area. Colin's parents are in their early sixties and wonder how long they will be able to manage looking after him without help. Mrs Grant in particular finds looking after Colin full-time quite stressful, and her husband thinks she may be suffering from depression. Colin himself doesn't have any friends in the area and gets bored and restless at home all day with his mother. On the other hand, his parents would like him to carry on living at home for as long as possible.

Imagine that you have been asked to assess the *needs* of the people featured in these case studies, based on the information given here. Read each of the case studies carefully, then for each one note down your answers to these questions.

- What do the people in the case study identify as their main needs?
- What other needs do you think they may have?

Comment   To help you with this and the following activities, I will use case study 1 as an illustration. These are the notes I made.

Mandy and Sean Brown's needs include:

- affordable childcare for Sean, so Mandy can go out to work
- advice/help for Mandy with claiming welfare benefits
- advice/support in treating Sean's asthma
- help with moving to somewhere less damp.

In carrying out this first activity you have already begun to practise a number of skills. The first stage in helping someone gain access to services is to *assess* their individual needs. In this brief exercise, you have had to elicit, or draw out, from the information you have been given, the relevant information and to make *judgements* about individuals' needs.

In a real-life setting you would obviously have access to more information than you have been given here. You would be able to interview individuals directly and perhaps draw on information from other sources. In the next activity you are asked to think about what *further* information you would need to have if you were making an assessment of the individuals in these case studies 'for real'.

Activity 2   **What else would I need to know?**

Allow about 20 minutes   Go back over your notes on each of the case studies in Activity 1. For each case, make a brief note of what else you might need to know if you were asked to make a 'real' assessment of that person's needs.

Comment   Here is what I noted down for case study 1:

I thought that I would want to know more about Mandy's partner, Gary, and the circumstances in which he left. Is the child his, and is he financially liable for Sean's support? If so, is he sending Mandy any money? Is he likely to return, and will this cause any problems for Mandy? Given Sean's problems with asthma, I thought it would be useful to know more about his medical history, and perhaps about Mandy's own. Her education and employment history might also throw up information that would be useful in helping her in the future. In terms of housing, I wondered whether she had ever lived in, or applied for, local authority accommodation, and whether she thought she was eligible?

I hope you managed to come up with at least two or three instances of 'further information needed' for each of the case studies. There is always a balance to be struck between the costs involved in obtaining information about an individual's circumstances and the benefits that such information might offer. Part of the skill in assessing a person's needs lies in picking out from the details of their life the information which will help you to make a proper assessment of their needs.

> **Key point**
> *   Assessing an individual's need for services involves paying close attention to the details of their circumstances.

Section 2
Sources of information

You should now have some sense of the *needs* of each of the individuals featured in the three case studies. The next stage is to think about how those needs might be met by health and social care services in the local community. But first, it will be useful to have a general sense of the *kinds* of services that might be of help to the individuals in the case studies.

Activity 3   **What kinds of services?**

Allow about 15 minutes   Having made a note of Mandy and Sean Brown's needs, I drew up a list of the kinds of services I thought they might need:

Needs	Kinds of services
Childcare	Nursery or childminder
Welfare benefits	Information/advice service
Sean's asthma	Asthma clinic or support group
Damp flat	Housing information/advice service

Look back over the notes that you made in Activity 1 on Mr and Mrs Bhatti's needs (case study 2). Then draw up your own chart matching *needs* to *kinds of services*. At this stage don't worry about trying to think of particular organisations or agencies, but think in more general terms. Then do the same for the Grant family (case study 3).

Comment   How did you get on with the other examples? Don't worry if you didn't know whether particular services existed, or who might provide them. The important thing is to have a general sense of what might help the individuals concerned. For example, for case study 2 your list may have included a need for meals-on-wheels or a home help, and perhaps attendance at a day centre for older people for Mr Bhatti. For case study 3, you might have thought of a day centre for Colin, as well as respite care to give his parents a break.

The next stage is to get a clearer sense of which organisations and agencies provide these services. Once again I have made some notes for case study 1 to give you an idea of the kinds of organisations that provide services.

Case study 1

Childcare facilities, such as nurseries, crèches and childminders, are provided by a whole range of organisations – some private, some charitable or voluntary organisations, some local authority controlled. But most childcare provision is inspected and approved by the local authority's social services department, so I thought they would be a good, central source of information.

Welfare benefits are the responsibility of the Benefits Agency, which is a central government agency, but has offices in local areas where people can make enquiries and claims.

How do you begin to find out about services in the local community?

Health services, such as those that might provide assistance with Sean's asthma, are now mostly under the control of local NHS trusts, but primary health care (as you saw in Unit 10) tends to be provided through local GPs' surgeries or health centres.

Housing is the responsibility of local authorities in Britain and the Housing Executive in Northern Ireland.

You can see that this list includes *statutory* providers, both national (such as the Benefits Agency) and local (the social services department, the NHS trust and the council's housing department), *voluntary* agencies and *private* organisations. (Earlier units in the course have made use of the term 'mixed economy of care' to refer to this diversity of kinds of providers.) Identifying the most appropriate service to meet an individual's needs will involve being aware of the range of providers in the locality.

Activity 4   Who provides the services?

Allow about 20 minutes   Who provides the kinds of services that you identified for case studies 2 and 3? For each of the services that you listed in Activity 3, try to write down the name of an organisation or agency that you think might provide this service.

    To help you with this activity, you may want to refer to Care in the UK. You might also make use of the course units that you have studied to date. I don't expect your notes to be as detailed as those I made for case study 1. And don't worry if you can't match a name to each of the services. You may have to make an intelligent guess at this stage – there will be a chance to check out your guess in a later activity.

Comment   How did you get on? It doesn't matter if you couldn't think of a service provider to match every kind of service you had identified. The important point to note here is the *range* of service providers that exists in any local area. For case study 2, you may have identified the local social services department as the first point of contact for information about a number of the services required by Mr and Mrs Bhatti, but you might also have thought of voluntary or charitable agencies that work with older people. For case study 3, social services would again be a key service provider, especially for respite care. Mrs Grant may need to see her GP about treatment for depression – but she may also get help from an informal support group for carers of people with learning difficulties.

Having considered the kinds of services that an individual might need, how do you go about gaining *information* about them?

Activity 5   Identifying sources of information

Allow about 15 minutes   For this activity, I want you to imagine that the individuals featured in the case studies live in your local area, close to where you yourself live. If you found yourself in the role of helping or supporting these individuals, where would you encourage them to begin to look for *information* about the services to meet their needs? Using the list you have built up of kinds of services and likely providers, make a list of all the possible *sources of information* that might help the individuals in each scenario. Try to think as widely as possible.

Although I have provided notes for case study 1, try to make a list for *all three* case studies, before looking at the comment below.

Comment   Case study 1

Thinking of the services that might help Mandy Brown, I came up with this list of possible sources of information for my own area:

- phone book /Yellow Pages
- Thomson Local directory
- local newspapers
- notices in doctor's surgery
- library
- cards in newsagent's window

- council offices
- Citizens Advice Bureau.

Was your list similar to this, or did you think of different places where you, or the people in the examples, could look for information? The kinds of sources you mentioned will vary, depending on the kinds of services needed and on the nature of the local community.

I hope your own examples helped you to see the *variety* of possible sources of information about health and social care services. Some of the sources you identified may be service providers themselves – such as the doctor's surgery or health centre. Others may be general information or advice points, such as the CAB or library, or even cards in the newsagent's window. Increasingly, new technology is changing the ways in which information is provided: some local authorities, for example, now display details of their services on the Internet, and computerised information points have begun to appear in libraries and elsewhere. At the same time, many sources of information can be found in your own home – these include local newspapers and directories, such as the phone book. In the next section we will be focusing on the kinds of information that can be gained from these sources.

Key points

- Health and social care services are provided by a wide variety of statutory, voluntary and private organisations.

- It is important to be aware of the range of service providers in the local area when trying to find services to meet individual needs.

- Information about health and social care services can be gained from a wide variety of sources.

Section 3
Finding out about services

Having located some possible sources of information, we now need to explore how *useful* they are in helping us gain access to health and social care services. The next activity, which is rather longer than the others, will give you 'hands on' experience of using some of these information sources. Obviously, it would take more time than we have in this unit to search through *all* the sources of information you have identified in Activity 5. To limit the scale of the exercise, I want you to use only those sources of information that you have access to in your own home or study setting. This will probably mean restricting your list to the phone book, Yellow Pages, local directories or guides that you happen to have, and recent local newspapers.

Activity 6	**Finding out about services in your area**
Allow about 1 hour 30 minutes	For this activity you will need to take each of the case studies in turn. For each one, use the sources of information that you have to hand to find out as much as you can about the services that each individual might be able to make use of if they lived in your area.

To give you an idea of where to look and what to look for, here are the results of my own search for information relevant to case study 1. Read through my notes before going on.

Case study 1

Before giving details of how I got on, it is important to say that I based my answers on the area where I live, which is a medium-sized industrial town in the Midlands of England. The town has a borough council and is also part of a shire county, which means that some services are also provided by the county council. The local government structures, and the kinds of local agencies that exist in your area, will vary depending on which part of the United Kingdom you live in and on the kind of area you live in – for example, whether it is urban or rural.

I took each of Mandy and Sean Brown's needs for services in turn.

Childcare provision
I started with the Yellow Pages. Under 'nurseries, child' I was referred to the entries for 'crèche facilities and services' and 'day nurseries'. The nearest crèche facility mentioned was in a neighbouring large town – too far by public transport. 'Day nurseries' was more promising – there was a long list of these, although on closer inspection only two in the town itself. I then looked under 'childcare', which listed crèches and day nurseries, and also gave details of 'nanny and childcare agencies', including one close by, but I guessed this kind of service might be too expensive for Mandy.

The Thomson Local directory had a section headed 'childminders', but there were only three entries, none of them local; it didn't list nurseries at all.

Having found out that childcare was the responsibility of social services departments, which come under county councils (or their equivalent), I looked up the county council in the front 'business' section of the phone book. There I found a full-page display entry for social services, which included separate phone numbers, at County Hall, for 'services for children, families and older people' and 'services for under eights and childminders'. I also looked in the main entry for the social services department and found a more local entry – in my own town – for something called 'Family Support Teams' and even an 'Under 10s Team', which I thought might be worth following up.

Benefits advice
Browsing through the first few pages of the phone book, I came across a list of national numbers to ring for advice on benefits, including the Family Credit Helpline, which looked as though it might be of use to Mandy, even if it wasn't a local service.

I then looked up 'benefits' in the front section of the phone book and found a display entry for the Benefits Agency, which is part of the Department of Social Security. This entry gave details of the address and phone number of local offices by post codes. There was also more information here about helplines, including one for child benefit.

This page also referred me to a separate entry on 'child benefit,' which gave details both of the national Child Benefit Centre in Newcastle, 'for enquiries about child benefit, one parent benefit and guardian's allowance', and also the Child Support Agency.

I looked up 'advice' and 'information services' in the Yellow Pages: there was nothing in my own town, but the neighbouring town had a number of information centres, including one specifically for young people. I was also referred to the entry on 'social services and welfare organisations', which mentioned a number of support groups, although none particularly relevant to Mandy's needs. I then thought that a Citizens Advice Bureau would offer independent advice, so I looked them up in the phone book and found that there was one locally.

Asthma support
When I looked up 'health' in the phone book, I came across a number of national sources of information advice, including a general Health Information Service. In the first few pages of the phone book I found a national asthma helpline. I thought that this might have been able to put Mandy in touch with more local forms of support. The 'health services' entry in the phone book listed all the local NHS trusts and referred to their entries elsewhere in the book. My own local NHS trust didn't have a specific entry for help with asthma (although it did for other conditions, such as diabetes and AIDS). However, it did give details of a community health clinic and a child development centre, where the local health visitors are based. I thought it more likely that Mandy's first approach should be to her local GP surgery or health centre: she would find out her nearest one by looking under 'doctors: medical practitioners' in the Yellow Pages.

Housing
I looked under 'housing' in the business section of the phone book, but this only gave details of providers of sheltered accommodation. But since I had an idea that housing was

provided by local authorities, I looked up my local borough council, which had a full-page display entry. There was a list of numbers for the Housing and Environmental Health Department, including a general enquiries number, as well as numbers for home improvement grants and other needs, which may have been of use to someone in Mandy's position.

Now carry out your own search for information for all three case studies. Make brief notes of your findings. You will need to allow a fair amount of time for this activity and to divide it up equally between the three case studies. Searching for information can be a frustrating task. Don't worry if you draw a blank for a particular service – leave it and move on to the next one.

Comment | How did you get on with this activity? If you live in a city or large town, you may have found a wider range of services than I did. I certainly discovered that my neighbouring larger town has a wider variety of provision – independent advice and information centres, for example – than my own area. On the other hand, if you live in a small town or village, you probably found it quite hard to find any services that were within easy reach of where you live.

My own experience of doing this activity left me with a number of thoughts. I found that it is quite difficult – unless you know exactly what you are looking for – to find out about health and social care services in your area, using the sources of information available to most people. My experience was often of trying several approaches – different 'key words', for example – before I hit on the right kind of information. Even then, it was easier to find out about services that were the responsibility of large, statutory bodies – such as county councils and NHS trusts – than about those provided by smaller voluntary or charitable organisations. For these, you really needed to know the name of an organisation, and what kind of service it provided, before you knew where to look.

Was this your experience too, working on the other case studies? Were there services that you tried to find out about, using the information sources you had to hand, but were unable to? Once again, in a real-life situation, with more time available and the opportunity to search more widely, you would be able to make use of a greater variety of information sources. The next two activities will give you a chance to think about other sources of information that you might use – if you had more time and were able to get out and about in the local area.

Activity 7 | Using information sources in the local community

Allow about 30 minutes | Scene 7 of the skills video is a dramatised version of case study 1, the story of Mandy and Sean Brown. In recording this scene, we have placed these characters in a fictional setting – the Manor Estate – and imagined that Mandy has to find out for herself about the services that may meet her needs.

As you watch the video scene, make a note of all the *sources of information* that Mandy uses to find out about local services. You may need to watch the scene two or even three times.

Mandy Brown calls in at the local health centre

Comment   Mandy calls in at the *community centre* on the estate, where she finds out about the local playgroup from Steve, the unemployed volunteer at the centre. Steve is also the means by which she finds out about the local health centre. The receptionist at the *health centre* provides Mandy with information about GP services, and it's also there that she picks up a leaflet about getting help with Sean's asthma. Later we see Mandy on the phone – we don't know exactly who she's talking to, but she's advised that she needs to contact the *benefits office*, and the local *council* about her housing needs. Finally, we see Mandy talking to an adviser at the local *Citizens Advice Bureau*.

Mandy made use of a number of different *kinds* of information sources available to her in the local area. They ranged from the very *informal* – dropping in and chatting to Steve at the community centre – to the quite *formal* – an interview with a professional adviser at the CAB. As well as *face-to-face* conversations, Mandy also found out about what was available by making *phone calls*, and by picking up *printed information* (such as the asthma leaflet). Although the video scene focuses on a specific example, it has given us some sense of the range of information sources available in any local area. The next activity will give you a chance to apply this to the examples you worked on earlier.

Activity 8   **Where else could you look?**

Allow about 15 minutes   Go back to the notes you made for Activity 7. Imagine that you had more time and were able to get out and about in your local area. What other sources of information could *you* make use of to help meet the needs identified in the three case studies?

Comment   In Activity 7 I found out about *some* of the childcare options in my local area, but not all of them. It was only when I rang one of the social services numbers in the phone book that they offered to send me a complete list of registered childminders and day nurseries in the area. The leaflet included some information about the approximate costs of different kinds of childcare – something else that Mandy would need to know. Perhaps if I had contacted the CAB in the town centre, they might have put me in touch with a specialist, independent source of advice about benefits. And I know from past experience that my local GP surgery runs a regular asthma clinic, and holds details of similar specialist services.

I hope you managed to think of similar possibilities for this and the other two case studies. This activity, together with the dramatised example in the video, should have broadened your understanding of the range of information sources about health and social care services available within local communities, and of the variety of ways you can make use of them.

Key points

- Finding out about health and social care services involves using a number of different sources of information and a range of different approaches.

- Information about services is usually available within the local community – sources of information may be informal or formal, and may involve face-to-face meetings, telephone contact or printed material.

Section 4
Reviewing your learning from experience

In this unit you have gained some experience in finding out about health and social care services in a particular local area, and attempting to relate these to the needs of individuals. In doing so, you have had a 'taste' of what it is like to be a potential service user or a care worker in the role of supporting a potential user, trying to gain access to information about service provision.

Before moving on to the final, study skills section of this unit, you will find it useful to *review* what you have learnt from your work on Sections 1–3.

Activity 9   Skills review

Allow about 15 minutes   Look back briefly over your notes on Activities 1–8. Make a quick list of the skills you think you have practised in doing these activities. (You may want to refer back to the idea of writing a reflective diary that was introduced in Unit 5 to help you structure your thoughts here.)

Comment   This was my list:

- assessing individual needs
- matching needs to appropriate services
- identifying sources of information
- using sources of information
- matching information about services to individual needs and circumstances.

You may have described the skills you thought you had practised in different ways. Whatever your answer, I hope you felt that, in carrying out this series of activities, you have been developing skills that are vital for community-based workers in health and social care.

As well as helping to develop your practice skills, your work on this part of the unit should have further increased your knowledge and understanding of the range of health and social care services, and the organisations and agencies that provide them. Your investigation of services in your own area will have given you a sense of the variety of providers in health and social care – not just national and local statutory agencies, but also a range of voluntary and private organisations, both formal and informal, large and small. Your work on the unit relates particularly to the fourth of the five principles of good practice, 'promote and support people's rights to appropriate services'.

4.1 Portfolio record

If you are keeping a portfolio record of your work on K100, you will want to add to it your notes from some of the activities in this unit.

In particular, it will be useful to include:

Activity 1 – checklist of needs and circumstances for the three case studies

Activity 3 – list matching needs to services

Activity 4 – list of service providers

Activity 5 – sources of information

Activity 6 – detailed notes on services in your own area

Activity 9 – list of skills.

Key point

- The process of finding out about local services and matching services to individual needs involves a range of skills that are vital for workers in health and social care.

Section 5
Study skills

5.1 Progress with your study skills at the half-way point

You are nearly at the half-way point of K100, so it's a good time to review your progress in developing skills as a student. Naturally, this is something only *you* can do, but the activities below will help.

Activity 10   **Have your skills changed?**

Allow about 5 minutes   Think first about how you would rate your skills at the time you started K100. Work down the left half of the table circling a score against each area of study skill. Then do the same down the right half of the table. Finally, for each skill area, subtract your score on the left from your score on the right and write the difference in the 'change' column on the right.

	At the start of K100					Now					Change
	very capable	fairly capable	so-so	rather weak	very weak	very capable	fairly capable	so-so	rather weak	very weak	
Reading	5	4	3	2	1	5	4	3	2	1	
Note taking	5	4	3	2	1	5	4	3	2	1	
Cassette study	5	4	3	2	1	5	4	3	2	1	
Tables and charts	5	4	3	2	1	5	4	3	2	1	
Study in groups	5	4	3	2	1	5	4	3	2	1	
Time management	5	4	3	2	1	5	4	3	2	1	
Keeping up morale	5	4	3	2	1	5	4	3	2	1	
Essay writing	5	4	3	2	1	5	4	3	2	1	

Comment   The 'change' column should now show those aspects of study where you think you have made most progress since February. Are there some areas where you have rated yourself two or more points better? In nearly three months that would be pretty good going. Even one point is a useful gain to have made. But what about the areas where you feel there is no gain? Should you be giving these more attention? I hope there aren't aspects of studying where your score is lower now than at the start. If there are, perhaps you should talk to your tutor about it.

Of course, if your ratings of your skills at the start of the course (left side of the table) are high then you had little room for improvement anyway and perhaps the study skills component of the course is not so important for you.

The columns headed 'Now' show where you think you still have work to do to strengthen your study skills.

Activity 11   Analysing your scores

Allow about 15 minutes   (a)   If you have some low scores in the 'Now' column get a sheet of paper and write those skill areas as headings down the side. Against each heading write a few ideas about how you could strengthen that skill area – such as experimenting with new approaches, talking to fellow students, asking your tutor, setting aside time to practise, or working with *The Good Study Guide*.

(b)   On a five-point scale give yourself a rating for 'confidence' as an OU student at the start of the course. Then rate your confidence now.

(c)   If you join up the numbers you ringed in the left half of the table (from row 1 to row 2, row 3 and so on) you will have a 'profile' of your view of yourself as a student at the start of K100. Get your study diary and scan back over the entries for the early weeks to see whether they match this profile.

Then join up the numbers to give your profile of skills as you see them now. Do your more recent diary entries match this profile?

(d)   If there are discrepancies between your diary and the profiles, how would you account for them?

Comment   (a)   Keep this sheet of notes in your study diary and look back at it from time to time to remind yourself (i) to keep working on these skills and (ii) of your plans for doing it.

(b)   Has your rating of your confidence increased since the start of the course? It could be that it has gone down because you were over-confident at the start, not realising what demands the course would make of you. Yet, now that you have coped with nearly half the course, you have every reason to be feeling more confident than in the early weeks. Many OU students say the growing self-confidence they experience as they confirm that they *can* study effectively at degree level is one of the greatest benefits of taking a course.

(c)   Did you find your 'profiles' interesting? They are not based on a proper 'test', of course – they simply tell you what you already thought. But you may not have thought so systematically before about where your strengths and weaknesses lie, and how they are changing as you study. The profiles are just a way of getting your ideas about yourself out into the open, on paper where you can look at them and perhaps rethink them.

(d)   Checking your profiles against your study diary is one way of re-examining your assumptions about yourself. You see yourself from a different angle doing these very different exercises. So which is the better view? Did you focus too much on your worries in your diary and forget your strengths? Are the profiles too crude to capture the variety of your capabilities? Perhaps you now have some new ideas about what to put in your diary.

> **Study skills: Being an insightful self-manager**
>
> As an independent student you have to be 'manager' of your studies and of yourself. In the study skills component of K100 we stress the importance of *reflecting* on yourself and your ways of working, so that you can think *strategically* about your studies – taking account of your personal aims and capabilities, instead of just ploughing ahead, following instructions and hoping for the best. Exercises like the diary and the self-rating profile are ways of trying to 'take yourself by surprise' – sneaking a look behind the established assumptions about yourself on which you base your daily life. They are meant to stimulate habits of self-reflection and self-analysis, and enable you to be a flexible and effective self-manager.
>
> **Study diary**
>
> You should have some interesting thoughts to put in your study diary this week after your work with these profiles.

5.2 The K100 examination

Having looked back to the start of the course, we now take a brief glance ahead to the end. You don't need to let the exam influence your experience of the course just yet. There's plenty of time later on. However, it's not a good idea to ignore the exam until the very last minute. As always, it pays to approach a study challenge with a *strategy.* So between now and the exam we shall periodically discuss aspects of exam and revision technique to support you in developing a strategy. We start with a general overview.

The nature of the exam

The first thing to say about the exam is that it is designed to enable you to do well. The course team does not believe in 'trick questions'. We want you to have every opportunity to use the knowledge and the writing skills you are developing throughout the course. Our ideal is that your exam result should be very similar to your assignment marks. If you are doing a reasonable proportion of the course reading and sending in your assignments then you are already preparing yourself well for the exam. Yet it is important not to be taken by surprise, so you need to familiarise yourself with what lies ahead.

Activity 12   **The guidance in the Assignment Book**

Allow about 5 minutes   To get a quick idea of the main elements of preparing for and taking the exam, read Section 5 in the Assignment Book.

Comment   As you see, the recommended source of further advice is *The Good Study Guide*. But you don't need to look at it yet (unless you are keen to). You will be working on it a bit at a time in future skills units.

The exam is designed to allow you some choice in selecting what to revise. The specimen exam paper will show you what to expect and guide you in working out how to revise. It is also an excellent tool for helping you to practise answering questions and to develop a technique for the exam itself. We shall be coming to all these things in good time. For now the main message is that the exam is not something to worry about. If you approach it calmly, realistically and strategically, backed up by advice in the course materials and from your tutor, you have every reason to expect to do well.

Special circumstances

If you have a particular reason for anticipating difficulty with the exam, whether because of disability or not being able to attend an exam centre, contact either your tutor or the Regional Enquiry and Advisory Service at your Regional Centre. Special arrangements can usually be made where circumstances require them. But they need to be set up well in advance, so enquire in good time.

5.3 Working with numbers

Now we turn again to table-reading skills. Unit 12 questioned how well the care services meet the needs of different minority ethnic groups. And in Unit 10 you saw the importance, within the UK care services, of access to a GP. Clearly, the access that members of minority ethnic groups have to a GP is an important issue to explore. To investigate this we can turn to a survey carried out for the Health Education Authority and the NHS Ethnic Health Unit by the polling organisation MORI's Health Research Unit. The foreword to the 1994 report, *Black and Minority Ethnic Groups in England*, describes it as 'the most important and comprehensive study of knowledge, attitude, behaviour and health status among black and minority ethnic groups in England' (Rudat, 1994, p. vii). Although the main report focuses on England, it also draws on a previous UK-wide survey (Health Education Authority, 1994). The figures I shall quote combine data from both surveys.

The report devotes a whole chapter to the challenges of constructing a sample to give an accurate picture for men and women of different age groups, within different ethnic groups, living in different parts of the country. The sample on which the findings are based was made up as follows:

African-Caribbean	708
Indian	1,017
Pakistani	927
Bangladeshi	665
Total	*3,317*

The report points out that:

> *The ... sample sizes for each of the ethnic community groups allow for meaningful comparisons both between the groups, and with known UK figures. Some of the individual sub-groups (especially Pakistani and Bangladeshi women aged 50 to 74 years) have very small bases. As a result some of the comparisons in this report will need to be treated with some caution.*
>
> *(Rudat, 1994, p. 22)*

The survey found that, as with the general UK population, a very high proportion of members of black and minority ethnic groups are registered with a GP (98 per cent of African-Caribbean and 100 per cent of Indian, Pakistani and Bangladeshi, as compared with 99 per cent in the population as a whole). It explores a number of aspects of access to GPs. For example it reports that:

> In the UK-wide survey 5% of the population describe physical access to their surgery as difficult ... The proportions who describe access as difficult are significantly higher amongst South Asians, particularly Bangladeshis (17% describe access as difficult).

> (Rudat, 1994, p. 60)

One of the tables shows that within the population as a whole about *half* of those who had access difficulties reported that their surgery was too far away. However *three-quarters* of Bangladeshis gave this as the reason. Also within the population as a whole a *quarter* gave poor public transport as the reason access was difficult, but 40 per cent of African-Caribbeans gave this reason (Rudat, 1994, p. 61).

The table we are going to examine looks at surgery waiting times reported by members of different groups.

Table 1   Average waiting time before seeing doctor (minutes)

		Women			Men		
Age groups	*All*	*16–29*	*30–49*	*50–74*	*16–29*	*30–49*	*50–74*
UK population	18	20	17	15	19	18	17
African-Caribbean	27	28	32	26	20	24	26
Indian	30	29	28	46	22	31	26
Pakistani	33	32	30	41	36	34	33
Bangladeshi	50	49	52	49	49	46	52

Base: All those who saw doctor at last visit

(Rudat, 1994, Table 36, p. 63)

Activity 13   **Getting the broad picture**

Allow about 15 minutes   People were asked how long they had to wait before they saw the doctor at their last visit. Table 1 shows what they reported.

(a)   How long on average do people remember having had to wait to see their GP?

(b)   In general, is age an important factor in how long people have to wait?

(c)   In general, is ethnic group an important factor in how long people have to wait?

Comment   (a)   On average people wait for 18 minutes (you look at the figure for the UK population as a whole, and for all age groups).

(b)   The answer is no. You need to look along the row of figures for the UK population and see how much variation there is from the average figure of 18 minutes. All the figures are within two or three minutes of 18. Women and men in the younger groups report a little over 18 minutes – and women and men in the older groups report a little under 18 minutes, so perhaps there is a slight tendency for waits to be shorter for older people. Or perhaps it's to do with the way younger and older people remember and report their waits. (These are not *actual* waiting times, but what people remembered when they were asked by an interviewer.)

(c) Here the answer is very clearly yes. You should be reading down the column of figures below 'All'.

Activity 14   Getting into the details

Allow about 15 minutes   Let's explore these differences in waiting experiences of ethnic groups.

(a) Write a sentence roughly summarising the figures in the 'All' column.

(b) Is age a factor in the waiting times experienced within the different ethnic groups? (Tip: the figure at the left of each row is the average for that ethnic group. Scan along the row and where you see a figure which is more than three minutes above or below, write a small +5 or –7 against it. Then you will easily see where the main variations are.)

(c) Looking across the table as a whole are there any age or gender groups within the ethnic minority groups who experience roughly the same waiting times as the general population?

(d) Are there any age or gender groups who experience particularly long waiting times compared with the rest of their ethnic group?

Comment   (a)   Here is my sentence: Although the average waiting time for the population as a whole is under 20 minutes, for African-Caribbeans, Indians and Pakistanis it is around half an hour and for Bangladeshis it is over three-quarters of an hour.

(b) This is quite a tricky question to answer. You need to look along the row for each ethnic group and compare against the figure under the 'All' column. The variations are not very great for Bangladeshis, but for the other ethnic groups there are one or two sub-groups which seem to stand out. However, there are no very obvious overall patterns.

(c) Young African-Caribbean and Indian men experience waiting times of around 20 minutes, which is roughly the same as the general population.

(d) Older Indian women experience waiting times a quarter of an hour longer than the average for Indians (46 minutes as compared with 30). Older Pakistani women wait eight minutes longer than the average for Pakistanis. Although older Bangladeshi women wait longer than either of these groups, it is an average wait within the Pakistani group. (We should remember here the caution about the relatively small sample sizes of these particular groups. However, differences as large as 8 or 15 minutes are not very likely to be just sampling errors.)

Figures like these raise lots of questions about why there should be such differences in reported waiting times and it would take a long discussion to work our way through all the possible reasons. The report itself says:

> *Previous surveys have shown that patients from black and minority ethnic communities are significantly more likely to attend open GP surgeries (surgeries which do not operate an appointment system) than comparative white groups ... The current survey supports these findings ... [W]hilst 79% of the UK population attend appointment-based surgeries, this falls to two-thirds of African-Caribbeans, and just over half of South Asians.*
>
> *(Rudat, 1994, p. 61)*

But the report also concludes that the differences in waiting times 'are too large to be accounted for by this factor alone' (Rudat, 1994, p. 62). Other possible factors include the extent to which different ethnic groups attend surgeries with a group practice or a single GP. However, neither of these factors seems helpful in explaining why older women in some ethnic groups should wait longer.

Exploring questions like these fully is a specialised field of enquiry and not one we can usefully dabble in here. However, we can draw the general conclusion that members of black and ethnic minority groups experience significantly longer than average waiting times when they visit their GPs.

Study skills: Scanning data for trends

The skill you have been practising is: (a) finding your way into a table and then (b) scanning it for blips and trends. Look at the box headed 'Blips' on p. 94 of *The Good Study Guide*.

1   The important first step was to recognise that the figure '18' at the top left was the UK average. All the other figures were deviations from this average.

2   The second step was to scan across from the 18 and down from it (the top row and the left-hand column). This quickly showed that variations along the row were small, while variations down the column were big. So age was not a major factor but ethnic group was.

3   You found that scanning down the columns for the different age groups was not very easy or productive because the differences are so big and uneven. But scanning along the rows showed you how much variation there was from the average for each ethnic group. Marking the main deviations on to the table quickly showed you that older Indian women were the group which deviated most sharply from the average for their group, and highlighted six other groups which deviated to a lesser extent from their ethnic group average.

5.4 Developing your writing skills

We have talked about getting the material together for an essay, but how do you actually put the words on to paper?

> **Study skills: Word processing**
>
> Do you write your essays by hand, or use a computer word processor? You can be just as successful with K100 either way. But certainly there are many benefits nowadays in using a computer as a study tool – and word processing is perhaps the greatest. It is not simply the look of the documents you produce, but the ease with which you can draft and redraft. However, you need to be able to type, or have the time to learn. And obviously there is the matter of what you can afford (with your OU fees to pay as well) and of how much use you would expect to make of a computer beyond K100. If you have reached this stage of the course writing by hand, you may well feel it not worth worrying about any new challenges until the course is over. (After all, you will be hand-writing your exam anyway.) But just to give yourself food for thought if you don't have a computer – or to consider uses beyond word processing if you do have one – read Section 5.4 of Chapter 3 of *The Good Study Guide*.

Finally, we continue the theme of developing your writing skills.

> **Study skills: What is a good essay?**
>
> In Unit 5 you read Sections 1 and 2 of Chapter 5 of *The Good Study Guide*, and saw some examples of short essays written by new students. The essays were taken apart and discussed in detail to see the good ideas they contained – but also ways they could have been improved so as to make the ideas easier for readers to get hold of. Section 3 of Chapter 5 draws together some general principles from that analysis of the essays. It provides a basic guide to what you should be aiming for in your essays. Read Sections 3 and 4 of Chapter 5 now. You may need to remind yourself of the essays by glancing back over Section 2.

> **End of block assignment**
>
> All that remains now is TMA 03 (you may already have started it). See how far you can apply the principles you have been reading about in *The Good Study Guide*.

References

Health Education Authority (1994) *Health and Lifestyles Surveys*, Health Education Authority, London.

Rudat, K. (1994) *Black and Minority Ethnic Groups in England*, Health Education Authority, London.

Acknowledgements

Grateful acknowledgement is made to the following sources for permission to reproduce material in this unit:

Text

pp. 184, 185, 187: Rudat, K. (1994) *Black and Minority Ethnic Groups in England*, reproduced with permission of the Health Education Authority.

Illustration

p. 171: Crispin Hughes/Photofusion.

Table

Table 1: Rudat, K. (1994) *Black and Minority Ethnic Groups in England*, reproduced with permission of the Health Education Authority.

Grateful acknowledgement is also made to the following sources for permission to reproduce the illustrations on the front cover of this block: all Sally and Richard Greenhill except *top right* Brenda Prince/Format and *bottom right* John Birdsall Photography.